The Man in
the Moone

The Man in the Moone

or

A discourse of a voyage thither

by

Domingo Gonsales
Thy Speedy Messenger

written by
Francis Godwin
(Bishop of Hereford, 1617-1633)

Logaston Press 1996

LOGASTON PRESS
Little Logaston Woonton Almeley
Herefordshire HR3 6QH

First published by Ioshua and Thomas Warren 1638
This edition and new Introduction © Logaston Press 1996

ISBN 1 873827 64 4

Typeset by Logaston Press
and printed in Great Britain by Redwood Books, Trowbridge

Contents

Acknowledgments

We would like to thank Hereford City Library for their help and time, together with Joan Williams of Hereford Cathedral Library and staff at the library of the Royal Geographical Society; the Reverend Tony Kelk, Vicar of Burghill Church; Bishop John Oliver of Hereford for giving permission for the use of the portrait of his predecessor, Francis Godwin; Ken Hoverd for all the photographs, excepting that of the Portuguese settlement on St Helena for which thanks are due to Trevor Hearl. Our thanks are also due to Brian Byron for the copy of Gonsales and his engine incorporated on the jacket, and to Michael and Mary at MYST in Weobley for further fun in finalising the cover. Finally, mention must be made of F.C. Morgan and his research into the background of the story.

List of Illustrations

1) Bishop Francis Godwin, from a painting in the Bishop's Palace, Hereford

2) Woodcut of Domingo Gonsales and his engine, printed as a frontispiece in the 1638 edition

3) The woodcut reworked and reproduced in the 1768 edition

4) Title page to the 1768 edition

5) The memorial to Robert Masters in Burghill Church

6) The globe which is part of the monument to Robert Masters. The form is unique, for the Duncan Liddel brass of 1613 at Aberdeen has a stand, but there is no map on the globe, whilst the Airay brass of 1616 at Queen's College, Oxford, has no stand though the map of the world has similarities with that of Masters

7) The Portuguese Church in Chapel Valley, St Helena. From a sketch by Jan Huyghen van Linschoten, 1589

8) 'Sugar-loaf Hill, St. Helena' by the Hereford artist James Wathen. This was painted c.1821 from a sketch made in 1812 from a point slightly to the west of that of van Linschoten's view on the previous page. From Gonsales' description his first flight was across the bay from the hill on the far right to that on the left

Preface

The text on which this version of Godwin's work is based is that published by F.C. Morgan in 1959. He in turn made use of a copy of the edition in the Smith College Studies in Modern Languages, published in Northampton, Massachussets, in 1937. That in turn was based on a copy of the first English edition then held in the British Museum. The intervening 1768 edition omitted various short sections of the earlier text, essentially those parts relating to an intended second story as well as some references to terrestial politics of the late sixteenth century and the more detailed notes on the Lunar language. These have been retained, but the text has been reset to include some of the easier phraseology used in the 1768 edition, as well as correcting what appear to have been some proof-reading errors in the 1959 edition. The text is also arranged into more suitable paragraphs, with modern spelling for the occasional word where it helps understanding, and modern use of italics. Otherwise the language and style of the original has been retained.

Introduction

The scientific background

'I will not go so farre as Copernicus, that maketh the Sunne the Center of the Earth, and unmovable.' So states Domingo Gonsales, Bishop Godwin's visitor to the moon. Clearly Godwin knew of Copernicus and his theories of the astronomy of the Solar System which had first been printed in 1543, shortly before Copernicus died. But what else would he have been likely to have known about the planets, the Solar System and theories of gravity when he wrote *The Man in the Moone*?

Duncumb, in his *Collections towards the History and Antiquities of the County of Hereford*, says of Godwin that 'some writers ascribe to him a knowledge of the true theory of the motion of the moon, long before it was generally known.'

The Dictionary of National Biography suggests Godwin wrote the story whilst a student at Oxford University, and particularly between the years of 1578 and 1580, some 15 years after Galileo's birth and 60 odd years before Newton's birth on Christmas Day, 1642. Even if he wrote it, as we suggest below, towards the end of his life, Newton was still to be born. The book was first published in 1638, five years after Godwin's death, when 'E.M.' was able to write in an introduction that '... the knowledge of this may seeme more properly reserv'd for this our discovering age: In which our Galilaeusses can by advantage of their spectacles gaze the Sunne into spots, & descry mountaines in the Moon.' It is evident that the calculations of Newton could not have been available to Godwin and that he had not had the use of a telescope.

The planets and the stars had long preyed on man's mind. The sun controlled the seasons, indeed life itself, and both the sun and the moon indicated the passage of time, the sun through the division between night and day, the moon from its birth, through to full moon and back again to a new moon. Man had long tried to use them, both to create a calendar and as a measure of time. Temples were built at Stonehenge in England, at Carnac in France, at Chichen Itza in Mexico, at Jaipur in India, in Egypt and countless other places, in an effort to devise formulae for the passage of time. It wasn't to prove easy. Modern measurement has established that the synodic month, the interval between identical phases of the moon, is 29.5306 days, whilst there are 365.2422 days in the solar year. The early astronomers were able to establish close approximations to these figures, but they realised that their 'rounded' figures led to errors which, whilst insignificant each year, gradually accumulated to cause shifts as seasons crept from one month to another.

Moslem culture based their calendar on the cycles of the moon. They made use of the calculations of the Babylonians who, 1,000 years before the flight of Mohammed, had managed to measure the lunar month to within an error of less than one second. The Moslem lunar calendar averaged each month to 29.5 days, by alternating 29 and 30 day months. To make up the majority of the balance, they divided the calendar into cycles of 30 years; for the first 19 years of each cycle the twelfth month had 29 days, for the following eleven it had 30. This left an error of only 3 seconds each month, taking some 2,500 years before it is wrong by one complete day from the initial cycle. However, being based solely on the moon, the Moslem calendar has 12 lunar months in a year, or 354 days. It is thus out of synchronisation with the solar year, against which it is some 11 days shorter. This meant that the seasons would drift, occurring in different lunar months as time went by.

The Babylonians had based their calendar on both the moon and the sun, and calculated that 235 lunar months equalled 6940 days, or 19 solar years, a cycle later called the Metonic cycle after a Greek astronomer. Inevitably, their calculations were slightly out: 6940 days exceeds 19 solar years by some nine and a half hours and 235 lunar months by some seven and a half hours. In practical terms, however, using the Metonic cycle meant that a lunisolar calendar could be based on a cycle of 19 years, and this is what the Babylonians proceeded to do.

The Greeks and later the Romans tried many other variations but including, for a while, a lunisolar calendar. The changes the Romans kept introducing, some for reasons of astronomy, others for political ends, meant that by the time of Julius Caesar the calendar year had fallen behind the solar year by about three months. The result was that June had all the characteristics of April and cooler weather did not start till December. This situation was resolved in 46 BC when Caesar introduced the Julian Calendar based on the sun. Three years of 365 days were to be followed by one of 366, the leap year, giving an average length over four years of 365.25 days. To bring the calendar back into line with the seasons, the year 46 BC had to have 455 days, with the new calendar commencing on 1 January 45 BC.

However, the Julian calendar has an inbuilt error that amounts to 1 day in every 128 years. Though this may appear to be insignificant, by 1500 AD the accumulated error had reached 10 days and had produced a noticeable effect on the date of Easter. The problem was resolved when a new calendar was introduced by Pope Gregory XIII in 1582. The backlog was resolved by omitting 10 days in October of that year, whilst the recurring problem was to be minimised by omitting leap years in 1700, 1800, 1900 and 2100. This reduced the net error each year to 26 seconds. In fashion with the current suspicion of continental European decrees, Britain did not follow suit with the Gregorian calendar until 1752, by which time 11 days had to be omitted to bring the calendars into line. Even then there were riots, with people clamouring 'give us back our 11 days!'

In performing all the astronomical observations that had led to these calculations, it had been a firm assumption that the Earth stood still and that all the planets, the sun and the stars moved around it. The philosophical Greeks often argued about which celestial bodies moved around which others, generally concurring with a static Earth. Their trump card was based on the wind and the performance of athletes: surely, if the Earth was spinning eastwards at some 1,000 miles an hour, then gale-force easterlies would constantly sweep the world, whilst jumpers in the Olympics would hurtle into the stands well to the west of their jumping-off points. No, the Earth must be static.

There was one dissenting voice to this earth-centric theory, Aristarchus. Living on the island of Samos where Pythagoras, some three centuries earlier, had put forward his theory that everything could be reduced to numbers, Aristarchus was much influenced by his theories. Aristotle was to write that the Pythagoreans 'saw that the modifications and the ratios of the musical scales were express-ible in numbers—since, then, all other things seemed in their whole nature to be modelled on numbers, and numbers seemed to be the first things in the whole of nature, they supposed the elements of numbers to be the elements of all things, and the whole heaven to be a musical scale and a number ... and the whole arrangement of the heavens they collected and fitted into their scheme; and if there was a gap anywhere, they readily made additions so as to make their whole theory coherent.'

Using geometry as the basis for his work, Aristarchus calculated that, although the sun and the moon looked the same size, the sun was nineteen times the size of the Moon and nineteen times further away from the Earth. Whilst his conclusions were quantitatively inaccurate (the sun is 400 times larger and farther away than the moon) his methods were sound. On this basis he argued that, just as it was illogical that a hammer thrower could throw a hammer several times his own weight, so it was for a larger sun to rotate around a smaller Earth. However, his theory was not taken seri-ously, as much as anything because the mathematics of a larger sun, with the Earth rotating around it, involved a universe far larger than man had ever before contemplated.

So astronomers continued to depict the universe as based on the centrally positioned Earth, with concentric spheres around it occu-pied by the rotating planets and stars. This was the basis of a model propounded by Ptolemy, working from his observatory on top of a temple near Alexandria, in the early second century AD. Over time this theory was adapted and amended by calculations and the intro-duction of epicycles to explain the observed differences, differences now known to be due to the heliocentric nature of the Solar System, the angle of tilt of the Earth, and the elliptical nature of the orbits of the planets as opposed to the circular ones used in the model.

The model also assumed that the Earth was spherical, which it isn't quite. (Newton was eventually to propose that it was slightly flattened at the poles.) Columbus' voyage westwards to find Asia was not intended to prove that the Earth was round (this was a myth accorded to his voyage that only grew in subsequent years), but that it was smaller than had been suggested. It was Ptolemy's maps that had helped convince Columbus that Asia could be reached in a westerly direction in a third of the actual distance.

When Columbus reached the Americas in 1492, Leonardo da Vinci was some 40 years old. He imagined what the world would look like from the Moon: 'If you were where the moon is, it would appear to you that the sun was reflected over as much of the sea as it illumines in its daily course, and the land would appear amid this water like the dark spots that are upon the moon, which then looked at from the earth presents to mankind the same appearance that our earth would present to men dwelling in the moon.'

These would all have been thoughts available to a man of Godwin's learning. Da Vinci's ideas were also available to Copernicus, then a student at the University of Cracow.

Born in 1473 in Thorn, on the banks of the Vistula, in northern Poland, Copernicus, on the death of his father when he was aged ten, went to live with his uncle, who became bishop of Ermeland. He studied mathematics at Cracow University, was appointed a canon in the bishop's seat of Frauenburg, then went south to Renaissance Italy to study canon law at Bologna and medicine at Padua, where he also attended some lectures on astronomy. He was also one of the first generation who could acquire books relatively cheaply, thanks to the advent of printing.

It was printing which partially led to the undoing of Ptolemy's great work, *Almagest*, or 'The Great Mathematical Collection'. Before this, any failings in the Ptolemaic system could be attributed to errors in transcription by one of the many scribes. With the printed word there could be no such excuse. Reading and re-reading *Almagest*, Copernicus became convinced of its fundamental errors. He tried placing the sun at the centre and re-worked the Solar System, only to find his model had almost as many flaws as that of Ptolemy. He then moved the centre slightly away from the sun, added back Ptolemaic epicycles to account for some of the discrepancies between the model and visual evidence, but still did not realise that the second major flaw in Ptolemy's model was that the planets have elliptical orbits, not circular ones. One major result of this is that the planets move faster when they are closer to the sun. Copernicus was quite old by the time he completed his heliocentric theory, published as *De Revolutionibus Orbium Coelestium*, 'Concerning the Revolutions of the heavenly spheres'. Although several churchmen, including Nicole Oresme, Dean of Rouen and later Bishop of Lisieux, had already refuted many of the arguments that proposed that the Earth must be stationary, Copernicus lacked the spirit to fight both the Catholic Church, with its desire for the Earth to be the central point of the universe, and the new Protestants, keen to put the word of the Bible above anything else. It was not until *The Man in the Moone* had been written that a new generation of astronomers began to resolve the problems of the Solar System, for Copernicus' system, like Ptolemy's, was full of faults.

Partly as a result of Copernicus' work, it became clear there was a need for more and better observational data to help determine the inter-relationships of the planets. Tycho Brahe (1546-1601) was a follower of Ptolemy, but had observed several times that the calculations he made from Ptolemy's tables turned out to be inaccurate when measured against observed events in the skies. Brahe's foster father died from pneumonia having saved the Danish king, Frederick II, from drowning. The king, to show his gratitude, compensated the young Brahe for his loss with a large grant with which he built the fine observatory of Uranienborg, on the island of Hven off Copenhagen. He acquired or manufactured the most up to date astronomical equipment which he brought to his base. The other facilities at Uranienborg included flush toilets, a printing press and paper mill, a chemical laboratory and even a private jail.

When the observatory was completed, the observations, which were much more accurate than those which preceded them, came pouring in. But Brahe was an observer and not a theorist: his major theory, in which the planets orbited the sun which then orbited the Earth, created as many problems as it solved. Brahe's careful and accurate measurements needed an expert mathematician to interpret them. In 1600, Johannes Kepler (1571-1630) joined Brahe as his assistant. The two quarrelled incessantly: Brahe was expansive and

Bishop Francis Godwin, from a painting in the Bishop's Palace, Hereford

Woodcut of Domingo Gonsales and his engine, printed as a frontispiece in the 1638 edition

The woodcut reworked and reproduced in the 1768 edition

THE STRANGE
VOYAGE and ADVENTURES
OF
DOMINGO GONSALES,
TO THE
WORLD in the MOON.

CONTAINING

An Account of the Island of St. HELLENA; the Place where he resided some Years in, and where he planned this Wonderful Voyage; his entering on Board one of the Homeward-bound *East-India* Ships for *Spain*; their running on the Rocks near the Pike of *Teneriff*, to avoid an *English* Squadron of Ships, that were in Pursuit of the *Spanish* Fleet; *Gonsales* had just Time to fix his Machine, which carried him in Safety to the Pike of *Teneriff*, having rested his Ganfas on the Mountain, whence was pursued by the Savages; when giving the Signal to his Birds, they arose in the Air with him for their Journey to the Moon: The wonderful Apparitions and Devils he met with in his Progress; their Temptations to him, which he avoided, and their supplying him with choice Provisions; his leaving this Hellish Crew, and proceeding on his Voyage to the Moon; his safe Arrival there; the Manners, Customs, and Language of the Emperors, Kings, Princes and People: His short Stay there, to the great Grief of the *Lunars*; the inestimable Presents in Jewels the Author received at his Departure; his repassing to our Earthly Globe again, and was set down in *China* by his Birds; his being taken for a Magician by the Country People, and preserved from their Fury by a *Chinese* Mandarin; his going aboard an *India* Ship bound to *Europe*; his safe Arrival in his own Country, where he made his Discoveries to the King of *Spain*, who held several Cabinet Councils to deliberate on a proper Use to be made of these Discoveries.

With a Description of the Pike of *Teneriff*, as travelled up by some *English* Merchants.

The SECOND EDITION.

LONDON:

Printed by JOHN LEVER, Bookseller, Stationer, and Printseller, at *Little Moorgate*, next to *London Wall*, near *Moorfields*. 1768.

Title page to the 1768 edition

HERE LYETH THE BODYE OF ROBERT MASTERS
GENT: LATE LORD OF THIS MANNOVR WHO TRAVEL-
LED W:TH THOMAS CANDISH ESQ:R TO VIRGINIA AND
AFTERWARD ABOVTE THE GLOBE OF Y:E WHOLE
WORLDE, & AFTER HIS RETVRNE MARRYED WINEFRID
Y:E DAVGHT:R OF THOM: CORNWALL OF BVCKLAND GENT.
BY WHOM HE HATH 2 SONES & 7. DAVGHTERS. HE
DEPARTED THIS LIFE THE 3. OF IVNE A:O 1619.

The memorial to Robert Masters in Burghill Church

The globe which is part of the monument to Robert Masters. The form is unique, for the Duncan Liddel brass of 1613 at Aberdeen has a stand, but there is no map on the globe, whilst the Airay brass of 1616 at Queen's College, Oxford, has no stand though the map of the world has similarities with that of Masters

The Portuguese Church in Chapel Valley, St Helena
From a sketch by Jan Huyghen van Linschoten, 1589

'Sugar-loaf Hill, St. Helena' by the Hereford artist James Wathen. This was painted c.1821 from a sketch made in 1812 from a point slightly to the west of that of van Linschoten's view on the previous page. From Gonsales' description his first flight was across the bay from the hill on the far right to that on the left despotic, Kepler neurotic and arrogant. But they each needed the other, the one the mathematical mind, the other the observational data. In the first instance Brahe gave Kepler the problem of solving the orbit of Mars. Being close to Earth, this planet had the most numerous and accurate data. Kepler, with his usual arrogance, said he would solve the problem in eight days; eight years later—some seven years after Brahe's death (as a result of a burst bladder caused by drinking too much at a royal dinner party from which he felt he could not excuse himself)—he was still working on it. Kepler tried over 70 different circular orbits. None matched the data. He turned the problem on its head and tried to plot the Earth's orbit from Mars. 900 pages of calculations later he was still no nearer the answer. Then he tried it from the position of the sun. At last he found the answer: the orbit was elliptical with the sun at one focus. He also established that the planet moved faster when closer to the sun, information that was to be used by Newton in forming his laws of gravitation.

But Newton had not even been born when Godwin penned his story. What was the extent of knowledge about gravity, as so visually portrayed by the bishop at the end of the sixteenth century when he wrote of Gonsales' journey to the moon, in his 'engine' pulled by his gansas, or wild swans, which floated weightless at a certain stage of the journey? '... O incredible thing! they forbare moving any thing at all and yet remained unmoveable, as stedfastly, as if they had beene upon so many perches; the Lines slacked; neither I, nor the Engine moved at all, but abode still as having no manner of weight.

'I found then by this Experience that which no Philosopher ever dreamed of, to wit, that those things which wee call heavie, do not sinke toward the Center of the Earth, as their naturall place ...

'Whereby it appeareth, not only that my Gansas took none other way than directly toward the Moone, but also, that when we rested ... either we were insensibly carryed, (for I perceived no such motion) round about the Globe of the Earth, or else that (according to the late opinion of Copernicus), the Earth is carried about, and turneth round perpetually, from West to the East ...'

Godwin comes down firmly in support of a rotating Earth. At the beginning of the seventeenth century Galileo was to ponder on this when he considered the many variations of the arguments debated by the Greek philosophers centuries earlier. If the Earth really does rotate, then why is it that arrows shot into the air don't fly off to the west, and why do easterly winds not constantly plague the land?

This was a time when physics was still dominated by Aristotle's view that heavier objects fell faster than lighter ones. However, it was then impossible to measure short lengths of time with any degree of accuracy, so Galileo had to resort to reasoning. He wrote in his *Dialogues Concerning Two New Sciences*: '[Were Aristotle right that] a large stone moves with a speed of, say, eight while a smaller moves with a speed of four, then when they are united, the [combined] system will move with a speed of less than eight; but the two stones when tied together make a stone larger than that which before moved with a speed of eight. Hence the heavier body moves with less speed than the lighter; an effect which is contrary to [Aristotle's] supposition. Thus you see how, from your assumption that the heavier body moves more rapidly than the lighter one, I infer that the heavier body moves more slowly.'

However, Galileo recognised that there was a critical difference, for if you were to be hit by the heavier stone then you would feel it more than if hit by the lighter one. He was half way towards Newton's concept of inertia. He groped towards the other half of the concept, that bodies once in motion tend to remain in motion, for he realised that just as it is more difficult to get the larger stone in motion, it is equally as difficult to stop it.

Considering the problem of the arrows in the air, and the jumping athletes, he considered the position of travellers on board a ship:

> Shut yourself up with some friend in the main cabin below decks on some large ship, and have with you there some flies, butterflies, and other small flying animals. Have a large bowl of water with some fish in it; hang up a bottle that empties drop by drop into a wide vessel beneath it. With the ship standing still, observe carefully how the little animals fly with equal speed to all sides of the cabin. The fish swim indifferently in all directions; the drops fall into the vessel beneath; and, in throwing something to your friend,

you need throw it no more strongly in one direction than another, the distances being equal; jumping with your feet together, you pass equal spaces in every direction. When you have observed all these things carefully ... have the ship proceed with any speed you like, so long as the motion is uniform and not fluctuating this way and that. You will discover not the least change in all the effects named, nor could you tell from any of them whether the ship was moving or standing still.

Galileo couldn't progress any further for his conception of inertia was that objects had a tendency to remain still. So a reader of the works of the time, such as Godwin, although aware of gravity as some kind of force, would also appreciate the pre-Newtonian, pre-Galilean, view that smaller bodies would exert a smaller force. Thus the Moon, being smaller than the Earth, would have smaller (gravitational) force allowing its inhabitants and vegetation to grow taller. It was over half a century after Godwin's death that Newton formulated his gravitational theory.

In *The Man in the Moone*, Godwin describes the surface of the Moon. It appears he hadn't made use of one of the then new fangled telescopes both from what 'E.M.' says in his introduction to the 1638 edition relating to the then increasing use of the telescopes (Galilaeusses as he calls them), but also from the description he gives. He says, through Gonsales: 'Then, I perceived also, that it was covered for the most part with a huge and mighty Sea, those parts only being drie Land, which shew unto us here somewhat darker then the rest of her body .... As for that part which shineth so clearly in our eyes; it is even another Ocean, yet besprinckled heere and there with Islands, which for the littlenesse, so farre off we cannot discern. So that same splendor appearing unto us, and giving light unto our night, appeareth to be nothing else but the reflexion of the Sun beames returned unto us out of the water, as out of a glasse: How ill this agreeth with that which our Philosophers teach in the schooles I am not ignorant.'

Godwin was writing at a time when use of telescopes was becoming more widespread, and it is perhaps surprising, seeing his advanced views on gravity and Duncumb's comments on his advanced views on the 'motion of the moon' that he appears not to have made some use of the instrument. Galileo, in 1623, wrote: 'We are certain the first inventor of the telescope was a simple spectacle-maker who, handling by chance different forms of glasses, looked, also by chance, through two of them, one convex and the other concave, held at different distances from the eye; saw and noted the unexpected result; and thus found the instrument.'

The most likely such spectacle maker was Hans Lippershey, a Dutchman living in Middleburg around 1600. Once one had been made and offered to the military for their use, others quickly followed suit. By 1610 telescopes appeared in Milan, Venice, Padua and were being made in London. Galileo started making telescopes in Venice, at first for the city fathers so that they could gain advance warning of any raids on their shipping, and then he trained them on the Moon. He found 'that the Moon certainly does not possess a smooth and polished surface, but one rough and uneven, and just like the face of the Earth itself, is full of vast protuberances, deep chasms, and sinuosities.'

He also discovered that Jupiter had four planets which circled around it.

> ...we have a notable and splendid argument to remove
> the scruples of those who can tolerate the revolution of
> the planets around the Sun in the Copernican system,
> yet are so disturbed by the motion of one Moon about
> the Earth, while both accomplish an orbit of a year's
> length about the Sun, that they consider that this theory
> of the universe must be upset as impossible: for now
> we have not one planet only revolving about another,
> while both traverse a vast orbit about the Sun, but our
> sense of sight presents to us four satellites [a term
> coined by Kepler] circling about Jupiter, like the Moon
> about the Earth, while the whole system travels over a
> mighty orbit about the Sun in the space of twelve years.

Whilst Godwin was proved wrong on his assumptions about the Moon's surface, perhaps suggesting that he hadn't had the use of a new telescope, his adoption of the Copernican theories and his advanced thoughts on gravity were subsequently proved right.

What is tantalising, is whether Godwin wrote the book as a way of setting out his theories on the relationship between the Earth and the Moon, and by inference the rest of the Solar System. If he wrote it whilst bishop of Hereford, which we presently reason, then he would have been writing at a time of gradually rising tension, both religious and political, which culminated in the Civil War. His published writings were fairly staid, and he may not have had the confidence or desire to put his position at risk by entering this particular theological minefield. He may have written it to satisfy his own need and in a way which would cause him least embarrassment if it came to light, and then stored it away to be found by his family after his death.

Francis Godwin and his friends
Son of the Rev. Thomas Godwin, later bishop of Bath and Wells, Francis was born in 1562 at Hannington, Northamptonshire. At the age of 16, he was sent to Christ Church College at Oxford where he appears to have written *The Mysterious Messenger, unlocking the Secrets of Men's Hearts*. He gained his BA in 1581 and commenced work on an MA in 1584 when he was described as 'one of the most ingenious persons as well as assiduous students in the university.' In 1586 he was a prebendary at Wells, and moved to Exeter as a subdean in 1587. Three years later he accompanied his friend, the antiquary Camden, on a journey in Wales.

He became successively a Bachelor and then Doctor of Divinity and in 1601 published the work for which he is best known, his *Catalogue of the Bishops of England*. This won the approval of Elizabeth I who promptly made him bishop of Llandaff. There was little pecuniary reward with this appointment, and he was allowed to retain his sub-deanery in Exeter as well as taking the rectory of Kingston Seymour in the diocese of Bath and Wells. Later he was also granted the rectory of Shirenewton in Monmouthshire.

During his sixteen years as bishop of Llandaff he improved his catalogue of bishops and collected information for a civil and ecclesiastical history of England. His revised catalogue was published in 1615, this time earning him the see of Hereford, where he became bishop in November 1617. However, his catalogues were not universally acclaimed. Several writers accused him of quoting other works without acknowledgement, of making chronological mistakes, of reliance on counterfeit charters and of giving 'false and imperfect catalogues in almost every diocese.'

He was also accused, whilst at Hereford, of using his power to place members of his family in positions within the Church. Browne Willis mentions that 'nothing is reported to have been in his gift but what he sold or disposed of, in regard to some son or daughter ...' Certainly, Dr. Thomas Ryves, an unsuccessful candidate for the chancellorship of Hereford diocese, petitioned Charles I in 1625 that Godwin had conferred the position on one of his own sons whom he complained lacked the relevant experience. He was also accused of selling the chancellorship of Llandaff.

Other sources are kinder. The author of the *Antiquities of the Church of Hereford* records that he was 'a good man, a grave divine, a skilful mathematician, an excellent Latinist, a great historian and an incomparable antiquary; a fine preacher, strict liver, diligent in his studies, and applying himself much to matters of religion.'

It was not until after his death in 1633, that *The Man in the Moone* was first published. It was an instantaneous success, with a further 24 editions in a total of four languages (English, French, Dutch and German) by 1768. The same year that it was first published, John Wilkins, subsequently bishop of Chester and a founding member of the Royal Society wrote *The Discovery of a World in the Moone, or a Discourse tending to prove that 'tis probable there may be another Habitable World in that Planet*. To his third edition he added a *Discourse concerning the Possibility of a Passage thither*, having obtained some ideas from *The Man in the Moone*. It is thought that Godwin's work also influenced Wilkins' *The Secret and Swift Messenger* about methods of communicating over distances, and works by Cyrano de Bergerac.

Godwin had married a daughter of the bishop of Exeter, by whom he had many children. One, Thomas, became chancellor of Hereford, dying in 1644. His brother, Morgan (1593-1645), became archdeacon of Salop. A third son, Paul, was apprenticed in 1628 to the important 'King's Printer', John Bill, who had printed several of the bishop's works. It was perhaps he who came across or was handed the manuscript of *The Man in the Moone* and helped prepare it for publication. There was also a possible family connection with Jonathan Swift, who may also have been influenced by the work. One of the bishop's daughters apparently married into the Swift family of Goodrich, where Thomas Swift, grandfather of Jonathan Swift, was the Royalist vicar in 1624-29. He was followed by a Thomas Godwin who served as vicar for four years before Thomas Swift returned for a second term, staying on until 1646. A Patrick Godwin then held the living from 1649-54. Thomas Swift's eldest son, Godwin Swift, certainly indicates a close connection with the Godwin family. He became a barrister and, upon the Restoration, served as attorney-general for the palatinate of Tipperary. There he was joined by his younger brother, Jonathan, whose son, also Jonathan, was the author and satirist. Jonathan the elder died before his son was born and Godwin Swift became partly responsible for the younger Jonathan's upbringing. In view of the close ties, including possible matrimonial links, between the two families, it would not be surprising to find that *The Man in the Moone* was part of Godwin Swift's library and thus featured in Jonathan's early education and led, in a small way, to the writing of *Gulliver's Travels* (1776).

But when did Godwin write *The Man in the Moone*? The key may lie in the remote island of St Helena and more specifically in a group of Herefordshire men who had a more than passing interest in the island and the future of English exploration. For St Helena is the island on which Gonsales first assembled his birds and his 'engine' in which he is eventually carried to the Moon.

St Helena was chanced upon by the Portuguese navigator, Juan de Nova Castella, on his way back from India. He landed on the island on St Helena's day, 21st May, 1502. For many years the existence of the island was kept a secret, being used as a port-of-call for Portuguese ships homeward bound from the east. The first resident was the unfortunate Dom Fernando Lopez who had deserted to the enemy during the Portuguese attempts to subdue Goa on the west coast of India. Although his life was spared, he had suffered hideous mutilations and, stowing away on a boat heading for home, he eventually abandoned ship when it stopped at St

Helena in 1516 and so became the island's first inhabitant. Although he once returned to Europe, he came back to St Helena and lived there for some 30 years.

The Portuguese used the island, with its abundance of fresh fruit, to put sailors ashore who were suffering from scurvy and other deficiency diseases, often leaving them there for several months before they joined another passing squadron. It was these sailors who built the first stone houses and a small chapel in the valley by the anchorage.

Though the Portuguese tried to keep knowledge of the island to themselves, its existence soon became more widely known. Captain Edward Fenton on a trading-cum-buccaneering expedition during 1582-3 knew of the island, for he planned to occupy it and waylay the Portuguese fleet returning from the East Indies, a plan he left untried.

However, it was not until 1588 that the English discovered the island for themselves, when Captain Thomas Cavendish landed there towards the end of his circumnavigation of the globe, the first English expedition to complete such a feat after that of Drake in 1577-80.

It is unlikely, therefore, that Godwin would have known of the existence of the island till well after he had finished studying at Oxford. But of greater interest is that at least two of the surviving members of Cavendish's expedition (and only 123 men set out) came from Herefordshire. (Others, killed on the journey, are stated as coming from London, Norfolk, Gloucestershire, Dorset, Corwnall, Weymouth, Newcastle, Plymouth and Sherborne.) Whilst bishop of Hereford it is quite likely that Godwin would have come into contact with at least one of them and learnt details of the island, allowing him to describe it in the detail he does. He also writes that 'most ships call' at St Helena, which would only have been the case after the beginning of the seventeenth century, reinforcing the proposition that he learnt about the island whilst bishop of Hereford.

Thomas Cavendish was born in 1560 at Grimston Hall, Trimley St Martin in Suffolk. As with many 'gentlemen' of the time, he took to piracy on the high seas. In 1585 he commanded a ship of his own in the fleet of seven vessels led by Sir Richard Grenville on behalf Sir Walter Raleigh which established the first colony in

Virginia. The fleet completed the voyage between the Spring and Autumn, capturing several Spanish vessels on the way home.

On his return, Cavendish planned his circumnavigation of the globe, closely modelling it on that of Drake eight years previously. His fleet consisted of just three ships, the Desire of 140 tons which completed the voyage, the Content of 60 tons, which was left with a semi-mutinous crew in the Pacific and of which nothing further was heard, and the Hugh Gallant, a 40 ton barque, which was scuttled near the Equator in the Pacific due to lack of hands to sail her. The expedition sailed on 21st July, 1586.

Having rounded Cape Horn his presence in the Pacific rightly alarmed the Spanish. Landing parties seeking supplies were harassed; in two skirmishes he lost a total of 24 men, almost a fifth of his crews. He plundered Spanish shipping until he felt sufficiently recompensed for his voyage, and then set sail in the Desire across the Pacific, and thence around the Cape of Good Hope. On 8th June, 1588, he anchored at St Helena, where the ship stayed for 12 days. On 10th September he arrived back at Plymouth.

One of the two accounts of the voyage was written by 'N.H.' It has been suggested that this is a misrepresentation for 'M.H.', standing for Master Hues, the mathematician Robert Hues who accompanied Cavendish. Whatever the case, Robert Hues was a contemporary of Francis Godwin and was born at Little Hereford in the north-east of Herefordshire about 1553, though he spent most of his later years in the service of the earl of Northumberland. However, he was at Brasenose College, Oxford, in 1571 and obtained his BA at Magdalen in 1578, just at the time when Godwin commenced his study at Christ Church. Sharing a love of mathematics, it is possible the two men knew each other and remained in correspondence.

In the north wall of the chancel of Burghill Church, there is a brass shield and inscription set in the original stone which is carved with simple interlacing tracery around a central shield. The shield contains a small brass with a coat of arms and at the bottom of the stone is an inscription on a second brass, whilst to the right is another brass plate that depicts a terrestrial globe on a stand. Part of the inscription reads: 'Here lyeth the bodye of Robert Masters Gent: late Lord of this Mannour, who travelled wth Thomas Candish

Esqr. to Virginia and afterward aboute the Globe of ye whole worlde, ... He departed this life the 3 of June Ao. 1619' having lived the rest of his life in Herefordshire.

It has been suggested that the Masters family had been resident for many years in Burghill, but there is no record of them before 1596 when this Robert Masters purchased one moiety of the manor of Burghill from Thomas Hakluytt of Eaton Hall near Leominster.

It is evident that Robert Masters went with Cavendish on the expedition to settle Virginia and again on the circumnavigation of the globe. He would have returned to England a wealthy man, able to marry into the local gentry and probably through his wife, Winefrid, acquiring the Burghill property.

Francis Godwin would have had two years whilst bishop to get to know Masters and to hear stories of the voyage. Perhaps they enjoyed each other's company at Burghill Manor, and at the bishop's palace at nearby Stretton Sugwas.

But there is yet another Herefordshire connection. The geographer Richard Hakluytt, a kinsman of the Thomas Hakluytt mentioned above, was born in Herefordshire and came from a family, probably of Dutch origin, which had provided sheriffs for the county from the reign of Edward II. He was also at Oxford, but had completed his studies before Godwin commenced his. In 1582 he published his *Divers Voyages touching the Discovery of America*, the first of many works on expeditionary geography and which soon found him arguing for greater English overseas exploration. What particularly appears to have roused him was reading, whilst in France, that 'other nations [are] miraculously extolled for their discoveries and notable enterprises by sea, but the English of all others for their sluggish security and continual neglect of the like attempts, either ignominiously reported or exceedingly condemned, and finding few or none of our own men able to reply herein, and not seeing any man to have care to recommend to the world the industrious labours and painful travels of our countrymen.'

In his preface to his *Principal Navigations, Voyages, traffiques and discoveries of the English Nation made by sea or overland*, published in 1599, Richard Hakluytt urges English sailors to turn away from their voyages to find northern passages, and instead concentrate on the warmer waters offering better prospects for the future. 'But alas our English nation, at the first setting foorth for their Northeasterne discovery, were either destitute of such cleare lights and inducements, or if they had any inkling at all, it was as misty as they found the Northern Seas, and so obscure and ambiguous, that it was meet rather to deterre them, than to give them encouragement.' He argued that the English had 'no Columbus' to follow unlike the Portuguese and Spanish, but that the nation's sailors should set 'course for the middle, lightsome, temperate, and warme Atlantick ocean ... [so as to benefit from] ... pleasant prosperous and golden voyages.' He remarks that whilst Spain had the Canaries as a useful Atlantic base, and the Portuguese the Azores, England had no equivalent. Was this another reason for Godwin to incorporate St Helena into his story, so as to urge the English to action?

Hakluytt used the narratives of Cavendish's voyages as sources for own his works, and may well have known Masters. For not only had Masters bought Burghill Manor off the Hakluytts, but had married Winefrid, who came from Buckland Hall, Docklow, only four miles from the Hakluytt home of Eaton Hall. With relatives and property in Herefordshire (his will tells of 'tenements in Leominster Ore') Richard Hakluytt may have visited Masters at Burghill. However, he died the year before Godwin became bishop. Even so it is not impossible that Godwin may have been inspired by Hakluytt's writing and his desire to see England more to the fore in exploration, and perhaps used a Spaniard, Gonsales, as his character in *The Man in the Moone* to inspire the English to greater deeds. There is an interesting aside when Gonsales talks of the Moon dwellers' customs. He tells of their love of tobacco and wonders at the connections between the 'Lunars' and the Indians of America. Is this another exploratory prompt?

Francis Godwin died in April, 1633, and is believed to have been buried at his residence in Whitbourne, near Bromyard, though no stone marks his grave. Duncumb, in his *Collections towards the History and Antiquities of the County of Hereford*, says that the only memorial was his coat of arms, *viz*, or, two lions passant, sable, a canton of the second with three bezants, impaled with those of the see, and painted in different parts of the church, with his enigmatical inscription underneath: Win Godwin all. Willis states that a monument, which may have been a cenotaph, in the lesser north transept of the cathedral, was shown as his in the early eighteenth century.

The terrestrial places mentioned in the story

Gonsales says he was born of noble parentage in Seville in 1552, and attended the University of Salamanca. He would indeed have come from a wealthy background, for the Spanish crown insisted that all trade with their growing number of colonies should be carried on through Seville and should be reserved for Castilians, as it was through their efforts that the overseas empire had been founded. The trade was regulated by the Casa de Contratación, or House of Trade, which had been founded in 1503 and the city prospered. From a population of 25,000 in 1517, it grew to 90,000 souls in 1594. Colonists paid for goods in gold and silver, and the city provided many of these goods through further trade with the Netherlands, then part of the Spanish Empire, and Italy, much of which was also under Spanish control. The huge quantities of money passing through Seville as recorded by the Casa de Contratación, rising from 1 million pesos a year in the 1520s to 35 million a year in the 1590s, was to cause massive inflation in Spain and several financial crises.

The University of Salamanca (about 100 miles west-north-west of Madrid) was essentially a theological college, but other subjects were also studied. Interestingly, it was here that the first quantity theory of money was advanced, whereby it is argued that money is worth more when scarce than when plentiful.

Gonsales leaves the university and heads to the Netherlands, arriving in June, 1569, where he obtains service under the Governor, the Duke of Alva. There had been ferment for several years in the Spanish Netherlands, partly over religious issues and partly due to rivalry between the nobility. In 1564, the Prince of Orange had been recognized as the leader of the great lords, but they were at loggerheads with the deputies in the provincial assemblies. The latter wanted a more liberal religious policy and the recall of the States General to deal with the country's myriad problems, whilst the Prince of Orange sought greater local autonomy for rule by the nobility.

All sides complained to King Philip II of Spain, who tried to negotiate a settlement, but Philip would not derogate control of the government to the nobles, nor would he consent to greater religious toleration. Revolution began, largely in the towns where the violent swings between boom and depression was currently at a low point in the cycle and people, faced with famine, had little to lose. In 1566, Philip sent the Duke of Alva, as his ablest general, with a large force of Spanish and Italian troops to reassert his authority. Alva did not finally arrive till August 1567, but then began a reign of terror. 12,000 people were tried and condemned for taking part in the rebellion, whilst some of the nobles were executed. It was when Alva tried to make the Netherlands financially independent of any call upon the Spanish purse and to pay for the presence of his army that further resentment was created. He proposed an import, export and sales tax of 10%, which met with a campaign of passive resistance. Armed resistance also grew, and for the next 16 years the Prince of Orange waged a land war from a base in his brother's principality of Nassau. But he was a poor general as compared to Alva, and was often leading ill-trained and ill-disciplined troops and it is not surprising to read that Gonsales was involved in one of the duke's victories. It was the Sea Beggars that was the main military force behind the eventual secession of the northern states, the future Holland, from the Spanish Netherlands. Raised by emigré nobles, and based in Emden, La Rochelle and England, they preyed on Spanish shipping and captured the sea ports on the Dutch coast. Alva's counter-offensive in the winter of 1572-3 was ruthless and he regained a number of towns, but the core of Holland and Zeeland remained impregnable to his land armies, protected as it was by rivers, marshes and the fleets of the Sea Beggars. In 1573, Alva was recalled, accompanied by Gonsales.

The setting for Gonsales' experimentation with his gansas and 'engine' is St Helena. *The Harleian Miscellany*, or collection of documents, contains information on this island which was used in the 1768 edition of *The Man in the Moone* and is reproduced below in the Harleian version:

'Before I come to relate the acquisitions of the English in India, etc., I will make halt at St. Hellens, or Helena; which is now possessed by the hon. East India Company. It is called the Sea-inn, because the English, and other nations stop there, as a place for watering and refreshment, in their long voyages to India. It was formerly seized by the Dutch, but retaken May the 6th, 1673, by captain Munday, with a squadron of English ships; and three rich Dutch East-India ships made prizes in the harbour: since which the company have fortified, and secured it, against any future invasion of Dutch, Portuguese or Spaniards. It is called St. Helena, by the Portuguese, who discovered it on St. Hellen's day; being April the second. There is no island in the world so far distant from the continent, or main land as this. It is about sixteen leagues in compass, in the Ethiopick sea, in sixteen degrees of south latitude; about fifteen hundred miles from the Cape of Good Hope; three hundred and sixty from Angola, in Africa; and five hundred and ten from Brasile, in America. It lies high out of the water, and surrounded on the sea-coasts with steep rocks; having within many cliffs, mountains and valleys, of which one is named Church-Valley: where behind a small church they climb up to the mountains. To the south is Apple-Dale, so called from the abundance of oranges, lemons and pomegranates; enough to furnish five or six ships. On the west side of the church, ships have good anchorage close under the shore, to prevent the winds which blow fiercely from the adjacent high mountains.

'The air seems temperate and healthful, so that such men brought a-shore there in a short time recover; yet the heat in the valleys is as intolerable as the cold upon the mountains. It commonly rains five or six times a day; so that the barrenness of the hills is not occasioned for want of water, of which it hath two or three good springs for furnishing ships with fresh water; the ground of its own accord brings forth wild pease, and beans, also whole woods of orange, lemon and pomegranate trees, (all the year long laden both with blossoms and fruit), good figs, abundance of ebony, and rose trees, parsley, mustard-seed, purslain, sorrel and the like; the woods and mountains are full of goats, large rams, and wild swine, but difficult to be taken. When the Portuguese discovered it, they found neither foor-footed beasts nor fruit-trees, but only fresh water; they afterwards planted fruit-trees, which so increased since, that all the valleys stand full of them; partridges, pigeons, moor-hens, and peacocks breed here numerously, whereof a good marksman may soon provide a dinner for his friends. On the cliff-islands on the south, are thousands of grey and black mews, or sea-pies; and white and coloured birds, some with long, others with short necks, who lay their eggs on the rocks, and suffer themselves to be taken with the hand; gazing at the surprisers, till they are knocked on the head with sticks.

'From the salt-water beating against the cliffs, a froth or scum remains in some places, which the heat of the sun so purifies, that it becomes white and good salt; some of the mountains yield bole-armoniack, and a fat earth like terra Lemnia. The sea will answer the pains of a patient fisherman, who must use an angle, not a net, because of the foul ground and beating of the waves; the chief are mackerel, roach, carp, but differing in colour from those among us; eels as big as a man's arm, and well tasted crabs, lobsters, oysters, and mussels as good as English.

'It is on this island that the scene of that fancy called *The Man in the Moon* is laid, written by a learned bishop, saith the ingenious bishop Wilkins, who calls it a pleasant and well-contrived fancy, in his book intitled *The Discovery of a new World*, or a Discourse tending to prove that it is possible there may be another habitable World in the Moon. Wherein among other curious arguments he affirms, that this hath been the direct opinion of divers ancient, and some modern mathematicians, and may probably be deduced from the tenets of others; neither does it contradict any principle of reason nor faith; and that, as their world is our moon, so our world is theirs.

'Now this small tract having so worthy a person to vouch for it, and many of our English histories having published, for truth, what is almost as improbable as this, (as Sir John Mandevil in his Travels, and others), and this having what they are utterly destitute of, that is, invention mixed with judgement; and was judged worthy to be licensed fifty years ago, and not since reprinted, whereby it would be utterly lost: I have thought fit to republish the substance thereof, wherein the author says he does not design to discourse his readers into a belief of each particular circumstance, but expects that his new discovery of a new world may find little better enter-tainment than Columbus had in his first discovery of America; though yet that poor espial betrayed so much knowledge, as hath since increased to vast improvements; and the then unknown is now found to be of as large extent as all the other known world: that there should be antipodes was once thought as great a paradox as now that the moon should be habitable. But the knowledge of it may be reserved for this our discovery age, wherein our virtuosi can by their telescopes gaze the sun into spots, and describe the mountains in the moon. But this and much more must be left to the criticks, as well as the following relation of our little eye-witness, and great discoverer, which you shall have in his own Spanish style, and delivered with the grandeur and that of glory, which is generally imputed to that nation.'

It is possible that this description is developed from that contained in the account of Cavendish's voyage written by Francis Pretie and contained in Hakluytt's *Principal Navigations*. This records that Cavendish anchored in a 'very faire and smooth bay under the Northwest side of the yland. ... The same day about two or three of the clocke in the afternoone wee went on shore, where wee found a marueilous faire and pleasant valley, wherein diuers handsome buildings and houses were set vp, and especially the one which was a Church, which was tyled and whited on the outside very faire, and made with a porch ...'

There was a house nearby providing an office through which a stream ran. The valley was full of fruit trees and herbs including a 'great store of lymon trees, orange trees, pomegranate trees, pomecitron trees, date trees, which beare fruit as the fig trees do ... parceley, sorell, basill, fenell, annis seede, mustard seede, radishes, ...'

After talk of the high and steep mountains, Pretie refes to the wildlife and mentions their tameness, as Gonsales found with his gansas. 'There is also Vpon this yland a great store of partridges, which are very tame, not making any great hast to flie away though one comes very neere them, but onely to runne away, and get vp into the steepe cliffes.' He also mentions pheasants, turkeys, goats and swine.

Earlier, it was noted that the island had been discovered by the Portuguese who had long kept its existence secret and had used it to help restore the health of their sailors on their return from voyages to the East Indies. In his *Principal Navigations*, Hakluytt tells of an unfortunate Englishman who was put ashore for the same reason. The account was related to him by Edmund Barber of Ipswich, who was one of the crew on board three ships under Captain James

Lancaster returning from a voyage to the East Indies in 1593. The ships 'directed' their course to the island, so its position was clearly well known to English sailors by that year. They anchored off the island on 3 April and stayed 'to great comfort' for 19 days. Barber went on shore and in a house by the chapel found John Segar of 'Burie' in Suffolk, who had been left 18 months earlier by Abraham Kendall, who had landed from the ship the Roiall Marchant and 'left him there to refresh himself on the Island, being otherwise like to have perished on Shipboard.' Barber recalled that Segar was in good health, 'but crazed in minde and halfe out of his wits', partly from the joy of meeting with others who were his countrymen. He appears to have chatted away and 'neither night nor day took any naturall rest, and so at length died for lacke of sleepe.'

When using his 'engine' to leave the ship that Gonsales was travelling on from St Helena, the gansas took him to El Pico on Tenerife, which Godwin indicates is '15 leagues in height perpendicularly upward, above the ordinary level of the Land and Sea.' Its height is in fact 3,600m, closer to two-thirds of a league in height, but it seems as if he may have obtained this information from Richard Hakluytt's book, which includes notes on Tenerife made by Thomas Nicols, an Englishman who spent 7 years in the Canaries. He mentions that Pico is 15 leagues, or 45 miles, in height and 'out of which often times proceedeth fire and brimstone, and it may be about half a mile in compasse: the said top is in some forme or likenesse of a caldron. But within two miles of the top is nothing but ashes and pumish stones: yet beneath that two miles is the colde region couered all the yere with snow, and somewhat lower are mighty huge trees growing, called Vinatico ...'

At the end of the 1768 edition of *The Man in the Moone*, there is a record of a visit to the mountain by English merchants during the reign of Charles II. It was during this reign that the East India Company, which had been incorporated during the reign of Elizabeth I, was granted a Charter allowing them to export a range of provisions free of duty. This gave a tremendous boost to the company's activity, further augmented after the Great Fire of London in 1666 when a number of families decided to emigrate and start afresh in a healthier climate, many settling on St Helena. Part of the account of the merchants' visit to El Pico reads:

'It cannot be ascended but in July and August, lying all other Months covered with Snow. ...

'About six in the Evening we began to ascend up the Pico, but were scarce advanced a Mile, when the Way being no more passable to Horses, we left them with our Servants. In the Ascent of one Mile, some of our Company grew very faint and sick, disordered by Fluxes, Vomitings, and agueish Distempers, our Horses Hair standing up like Bristles, and calling for some of our Wine carried in small Barrels on an Horse, we found it so wonderfully cold, that we could not drink it till we had made a Fire to warm it, notwithstanding the Air was very calm and moderate, but when the Sun was set, it began to blow with such Violence, and grew so cold, that taking up our Lodging among the hollow Rocks, we were necessitated to keep Fires in the Mouths of them all Night.

'About four in the Morning we began to mount again, and being come another Mile up, one of our Company failed and was able to proceed no further: Here began the black Rocks; the rest of us pursued our Journey till we came to the Sugar Loaf, where we began to travel again in a white Sand, being fitted with Shoes, whose single Soles are made a Finger broader than the upper Leathers, to encounter this difficult Passage: Having ascended as far the black Rocks, which lay all flat like a plain Floor, we climbed within a Mile of the very Top of the Pico, and at last we attained the Summit, where we found no such Smoak as appeared a little below, but a continual Perspiration of a hot and sulphureous Vapour that made our Faces extremely sore; all this way we found no considerable Alteration of the Air, and very little Wind, but on the Top it was so impetuous, that we had much ado to stand against it whilst we drank K. Charles II Health, and fired each of us a Gun. Here also we took our Dinner, but found that our strong Waters had lost their Virtue, and were almost insipid, while our Wine was more brisk and spirituous than before: The Top on which we stood being not above a Yard broad, is the Brink of a Pit called the Caldera, which we judged to be a Musket Shot over, and near fourscore Yards deep, in form of a Cone, hollow within like a Kettle, and covered over with small loose Stones mixed with Sulphur and Sand, from among which issued divers Spiracles of Smoak and Heat, which being stirred with any Thing puffs and makes a Noise, and is so offensive, that we were even suffocated with the sudden rising of Vapors, upon removing one of these Stones, which were so hot as not easily to be handled; we descended not above four or five Yards into the Caldera or Caldron, because of the Slipperiness under Foot, and the Difficulty; but some have adventured to the Bottom: Other Matters observable we discovered none, besides a clear sort of Sulphur which lay like Salt upon the Stones. ...

'No trees, Herbs nor Shrubs did we find in all the Passage, but Pines, and among the whiter Sands a kind of Broom being a bushy Plant: It is the Opinion of some ingenious Persons who have lived twenty Years upon the Place, that the whole Island being a Soil mightily impregnated with Brimstone, did in former Times take Fire, and blow up all or near all at the same Time; and that many Mountains of huge Stones calcined and burnt, which appear all over this Island, especially in the South-West Part of it, were cast up and raised out of the Bowels of the Earth at the Time of that general Conflagration; and that the greatest Quantity of this Sulphur lying about the Center of the Island raised up the Pico to that Height at which it is now seen; which appears by the Situation of those Rocks that lye three or four Miles round the Bottom of the Pico, and in such Order one above another almost to the Sugar Loaf, as it is called, as if the whole ground swelling and rising up together by the Ascension of the Brimstone, the Torrents and Rivers of it did with a sudden Eruption roul and tumble them down from the rest of the Rocks; especially to the South-West, where from the Top of the Pico to the Sea coast lie huge Heaps of these burnt Rocks one under another, and there still remain the very Tracks of the Brimstone Rivers as they ran over this Quarter of the Island which hath so wasted the Ground, beyond Recovery, that nothing can be made to grow there but Broom.'

Godwin makes China the destination for Gonsales' return flight from the Moon. If we are correct in thinking that he obtained much of his geographical information from Hakluytt, then it is interesting to note that Hakluytt also records some news of China in his *Principal Navigations*. One paper is a record made by some Portuguese who had spent some time imprisoned in China. This mentions that it was a country with large cities. 'The city Pachin, where the king maketh his abode, is so great, that to go from one side to the other, besides the suburbs, the which are greater than the city it selfe, it requireth one whole day on horseback. ... In the suburbs be many wealthy merchants of all sorts.

'... They have moreover one thing very good, and that which made us all to marveile at them being Gentiles: namely that there be hospitals in all their Cities, always full of people, we neuere saw any poore body begge.'

They also mentioned that there was freedom of religion, but that the 'moors' were having problems trying to convince the Chinese that they shouldn't eat pork.

A further article on China was printed in Latin in Macao in 1590. This mentions that as the king ruled over so many provinces, a number of magistrates were created to administer public affairs and justice. Some Fathers of the Society of Jesus (members of which order Gonsales eventually meets in Peking) are mentioned as having been trying to establish a mission in China for some 30 years, but owing to the Chinese dislike of admitting foreigners unless they were ambassadors, and also because of the perceived Christian attitude of condemning other nations, they were having little success. However, in 1583, two fathers were admitted to Xauquin, before being moved to Xaucheo.

The Portuguese trading post at Macao long remained the main contact with China until around the time of bishop Godwin's tenure of the see of Hereford. It was during this time that the Dutch seized Formosa and trade with the East was increasing. As with his use of St Helena in the story, perhaps Godwin was calling for greater English enterprise in the direction of China.

Andy Johnson & Ron Shoesmith
October 1996

THE MAN IN THE MOONE

It is well enough and sufficiently knowne to all the countries of Andalucia, that I Domingo Gonsales, was borne of Noble parentage, and that in the renowned City of Seville, to wit in the yeare 1552, my Father's name being Therrando Gonsales, (that was neere kinsman by the mothers side unto Don Pedro Sanchez that worthy Count of Almanera,) and as for my Mother, she was the daughter of the Reverend and famous Lawyer, Otho Perez de Sallaveda, Governour of Barcellona, and Corrigidor of Biscay: being the youngest of 17 Children they had, I was put to schoole, and intended by them unto the Church. But our Lord purposing to use my service in matters of farre other nature and quality, inspired me with spending some time in the warres. It was at the time that Don Ferrando, the Noble and thrice renowned Duke D'Alva, was sent into the Low Countries, viz. the yeare of Grace 1568.

I then following the current of my foresaid desire, leaving the Universitie of Salamanca, (whither my Parents had sent mee) without giving knowledge unto any of my dearest friends, got mee through France, unto Antwerp, where in the moneth of June 1569, I arrived in something poore estate. For having sold my Bookes and Bedding, with such other stuffe as I had, which happily yeelded me some 30 ducats and borrowed of my father's friends some 20 more, I bought mee a little nagge with which I travelled more thriftily than young Gentlemen are wont ordinarily to doe: Untill at last arriving within a league of Antwerp,

1

certaine of the cursed Geuses set upon mee, and bereaved me of Horse, monie, and all: Whereupon I was faine (through want and necessitie,) to enter into the service of Marshall Cossey a French Nobleman, whom I served truly in honourable place, although mine enemies gave it out to my disgrace that I was his horse-keeper's boy. But for that matter I shall referre my selfe unto the report of the Count Mansfield, Mounsieur Tavier, and other men of knowne worth and estimation; who have often testified unto many of good credit yet living, the very truth in that behalfe, which indeed is this, that Mounsieur Cossey, who about that time had been sent Embassador unto the Duke D'Alva, Governour of the Low Countries, he I say, understanding the Nobility of my birth, and my late misfortune; thinking it would bee no small honour to him to have a Spanyard of that qualitie about him, furnished mee with horse, armour, and whatsoever I wanted, using my service in nothing so much (after once I had learned the French tongue) as writing his Letters, because my hand indeed was then very faire. In the time of warre, if upon necessitie I now and then dressed mine owne Horse, it ought not to be cast in my teeth, seeing I hold it the part of a Gentleman, for setting forward the service of his Prince, to submit himselfe unto the vilest office.

The first expedition I was in, was against the Prince of Orange, at what time the Marshall my friend aforesaid, met him making a roade into France, and putting him to flight, chased him even unto the walls of Cambray. It was my good hap at that time to defeat a horseman of the enemy, by killing his Horse with my pistoll, which falling upon his leg, so as he could not stirre, hee yeelded himselfe to my mercie; but I knowing mine owne weaknesse of bodie, and seeing him a lustie tall fellow, thought it my surest way to dispatch him, which having done, I rifled him of a chaine, monie, and other things to the value of 200 ducats: no sooner was that money in my purse, but I began to resume the remembrance of my nobilitie, and giving unto Monsieur Cossey the Besa Los Manos, I got my selfe imediately unto the Duke's court, where were divers of my kindred, that (now they saw my purse full of good Crownes) were ready enough to take knowledge of mee; by their meanes I was

2

received into pay, and in the processe of time obtained a good degree of favour with the Duke, who sometimes would jest a little more broadly at my personage than I could well brook. For although I must acknowledge my stature to be so little, as no man there is living I thinke lesse, yet in asmuch as it was the work of God, and not mine, hee ought not to have made that a meanes to dishonour a Gentleman with all. And those things which have happened unto mee, may bee an example, that great and wonderfull things may be performed by the most unlikely bodies, if the mind be good, and the blessing of our Lord doe second and follow the endeavours of the same.

Well, howsoever the Duke's merriments went against my stomacke, I framed my selfe the best I could to dissemble my discontent, and by such my patience accomodating my selfe also unto some other his humors, so wan his favour, as at his departure home into Spaine, (whither I attended him) the Yeare 1573 by his favour and some other accidents, (I will say nothing of my owne industry, wherein I was not wanting to my selfe) I was able to carry home in my purse the value of 3,000 Crownes.

At my returne home my Parents, that were marvellously displeased with my departure, received mee with great joy; and the rather, for that they saw I brought with mee meanes to maintaine my selfe without their charge, having a portion sufficient of mine owne, or lessening the portions of my Brothers and Sisters. But fearing I would spend it as lightly as I got it, they did never leave importuning mee, till I must needs marry the daughter of a Portugais, a Merchant of Lisbon, a man of great wealth and dealings, called Iohn Figueres. Therein I satisfied their desire, and putting not onely my marriage money, but also a good part of mine owne Stock into the hands of my father in Law, or such as hee wished mee unto, I lived in good sort, even like a Gentleman, with great content for divers yeares.

At last it fell out, that some disagreement happened between me and one Pedro Delgades a Gentleman of my kinne, the causes whereof are needlesse to be related, but so farre this dissention grew betweene us, as when no mediation of friends could appease the same, into the field wee went together alone with our Rapiers, where my chance was to kill him, being a man of great strength, and tall stature. But what I wanted of him in strength, I supplied with courage, and my nimblenesse more than countervailed his stature. This fact being committed in Carmona, I fled with all the speed I could to Lisbon, thinking to lurke with some friend of my Father in-lawes, till the matter might bee compounded, and a course taken for a sentence of Acquittall by consent of the prosecutors. This matter fell out in the Year 1596, at which time that a certaine great Count of ours came home from the West-Indies, in triumphant manner, boasting and sending out his declarations in print, of a great victory hee had obtained against the English, neere the Isle of Pines. Whereas the truth is, he got of the English nothing at all in that Voyage, but blowes and a great losse.

Would to God that lying and Vanitie had beene all the faults he had; his covetousnesse was like to bee my utter undoing, although since it hath proved a meanes of eternizing my name for ever with all Posteritie, (I verily hope) and to the unspeakable good of all mortall men, that in succeeding ages the world shall have, if at the leastwise it may please God that I doe returne safe home againe into my Countrie, to give perfect instructions how those admirable devices, and past all credit of possibilitie, which I have light upon, may be imparted unto publique use. You shal then see men to flie from place to place in the ayre; you shall be able, (without moving or travailing of any creature,) to send messages in an instant many Miles off, and receive answer againe immediately; you shall bee able to declare your minde presently unto your friend, being in some private and remote place of a populous Citie, with a number of such like things: but that which far surpasseth all the rest, you shall have notice of a new World, of many most rare and incredible secrets of Nature, that all the Philosophers of former ages could never so much as dreame off. But I must me advised, how I be over-liberall, in publishing these wonderfull mysteries, till the Statesmen have considered how farre the use of these things may stand with the Policy and good government of our Countrey, as also with the Fathers of the Church, how the publication of them, may not prove prejudiciall to the affaires of the Catholique faith and Religion, which I am taught (by those wonders I have seen above any mortall man that hath lived in many ages past) with all my best endeavours to advance, without all respect of temporall good, and soe I hope I shall.

But to goe forward with my narration, so it was that the bragging Captaine above named, made shew of great discontentment, for the death of the said Delgades, who was indeed some kinne unto him. Howbeit hee would have been intreated, so that I would have given him no lesse than 1,000 Ducats (for his share) to have put up his Pipes, and surceased all suite in his Kinsman's behalfe; I had by this time (besides a wife) two sonnes, whom I liked not to beggar by satisfying the desire of this covetous braggart and the rest, and therefore constrained of necessity to take another course, I put my selfe in a good Caricke that went for the East Indies, taking with me the worth of 2,000 Ducats to traffique withall, being yet able to leave so much more for the estate of my wife and children, whatsoever might become of me, and the goods I carried with me.

In the Indies I prospered exceeding well, bestowing my stocke in Jewells, namely, for the most part in Diamonds, Emeraulds, and great Pearle; which I bought at such easy rates, that my stocke being safely returned into Spaine, (so I heard it was) must needs yeeld ten for one. But my selfe upon my way homeward soone after we had doubled the East of Buena Speranza, fell grievously sicke for many daies, making account by the same sicknesse to end my life, which undoubtedly had happened, had we not (even then as we did) recovered that same blessed Isle of S. Hellens, the only paradice, I thinke, that the earth yeeldeth, of the healthfulnesse of the Aire there, the fruitfulnesse of the soile, and the abundance of all manner of things necessary for sustaining the life of man, what should I speake, seeing there is scant a boy in all Spaine, that hath not heard of the same? I cannot but wonder, that our King in his Wisdome hath not thought fit to plant a Colony, and to fortifie in it, being a place so necessary for refreshing of all travaillers out of the Indies, so as it is hardly possible to make a Voyage thence, without touching there.

It is situate in the Latitude of 16 degrees to the South, and is about 3 Leagues in compasse, having no firme land or continent within 300 leagues, nay not so much as an Island within 100 leagues of the same, so that it may seeme a miracle of Nature, that out of so huge and tempestuous an Ocean, such a little peece of ground should arise and discover it selfe. Upon the South side there is a very good harbour, and neere unto the same divers edifices built by the Portuguese to entertaine passengers, amongst the which there is a pretty Chappell handsomly beautified with a Tower, having a faire Bell in the same. Neere unto this housing there is a pretty Brooke of excellent fresh water, divers faire walkes made by hand, and set along upon both sides, with fruit-Trees, especially Oranges, Limmons, Pomgranats, Almonds, and the like, which beare Fruit all the yeare long, as doe also the fig-Trees, Vines, Peare-Trees, (whereof there are divers sorts,) Palmitos, Cocos, Olives, Plumms; also I have seene there such as wee call Damaxaelas, but few; as or Apples I dare say there are none at all; of garden Hearbs there is good store, as of Parsely, Cole-worts, Rosemary, Mellons, Gourds, Lettice, and the like; Corne likewise growing of it selfe, incredible plenty, with Wheate, Pease, Barley, and almost all kinde of Pulse; but cheifly it aboundeth with Cattell, and Fowle, as Goates, Swine, Sheepe, and Horses, Partridges, wilde Hens, Phesants, Pigeons, and wild Fowle, beyond all credit: especially there are to be seene about the Moneths of February, and March, huge flocks of a certaine kinde of wild Swans (of which I shall have cause heerafter to speake more) that like unto our Cuckoes, and Nightingales, at a certaine season of the yeare, doe vanish away, and are no more to be seene.

On this blessed Island did they set mee ashore with a Negro to attend me, where, praised bee God, I recovered my health, and continued there for the space of one whole yeare, solacing my slfe (for lacke of humane society) with Birds, and brute beasts, as for Diego (so was the Blackmoore called), he was constrained to live at the West end of the Island in a Cave, Because being, alwayes together, victuals would not have fallen out so plenty: if the Hunting or the Fowling of the one had succeded well, the other would finde means to invite him, but if it were scant with both, we were faine both to bestirre our selves; marry that fell out very seldome, for that no creatures there doe any whit more feare a man, then they doe a Goate or a Cow; by reason thereof I found meanes easily to make tame divers sorts both of Birds and Beasts, which I did in short time, onely by muzzeling them, so as till they came either unto me, or else Diego, they could not feede. At first I tooke great pleasure in a kinde of Partridges, of which I made great use, as also of a tame Fox I had. For whensoever I had any occasion to conferre with Diego, I would take me one of them, being hungry, and tying a note about his necke, beat him from me, whereupon strait they would away to the Cave of Diego, and if they found him not there, still would they beat up and downe all the West end of the Island, till they had hunted him out; yet this kinde of conveyance not being without some inconvenience needlesse heere to be recited; after a certaine space I perswaded Diego (who though hee were a fellow of good parts, was ever content to be ruled by me), to remove his habitation unto a promontory or cape upon the North-West part of the Island, being, though a league off, yet within sight of my house and Chappell; and then, so long as the weather was faire, we could at all times by signalls, declare our minds each to other in an instant, either by night, or by day; which was a thing I tooke great pleasure in.

If in the night season I would signifie any thing to him, I used to set up a light in the Tower or place where our bell hung: It is a pretty large roome, having a faire window well glassed, and the walls within being plaistered, were exceeding white; by reason thereof, though the light were but small it gave a great shew, as also it would have done much further off if need had beene. This light after I had let stand some halfe houre, I used to cover: and then if I saw any signall of light againe from my companion at the cape, I knew that he waited for my notice, which perceiving, by hiding and shewing my light, according to a certaine rule and agreement between us, I certified him of what I pleased: The like course I tooke in the day to advertise him of my pleasure, sometimes by smoke, sometimes by dust, sometimes by a more refined and effectual way.

But this Art containeth more mysteries then are to be set downe in a few words: Hereafter I will perhaps afford a discourse for it of purpose, assuring my selfe that it may prove exceedingly profitable unto mankind, being rightly used and well imployed: for that which a messenger cannot performe in many dayes, this may dispatch in a peece of an houre. Well, I notwithstanding after a while grew weary of it, as being too painfull for me, and betooke me againe to my winged messengers.

Upon the Sea shore, especially about the mouth of our River, I found great store of a certain kinde of wild Swan (before mentioned) feeding almost altogether upon the prey, and (that which is somewhat strange,) partly of Fish, partly of Birds, having (which is also no lesse strange) one foote with Clawes, talons, and pounces, like an Eagle, and the other whole like a Swan or water fowle. These birds using to breed there in infinite numbers, I tooke some 30 or 40 young ones of them, and bred them up by hand partly for my recreation, partly also as having in my head some rudiments of that device, which afterward I put in practise. These being strong and able to continue a great flight, I taught them first to come at call affarre off, not using any noise but onely the shew of a white Cloth. And surely in them I found it true that is delivered by Plutarch, how 'that creatures which eat flesh are more docile than others'. It were a wonder to tell what trickes I had taught them, by that time they were a quarter old; amongst other things I used them by little and little to fly with burthens, wherein I them able above all credit, and brought them to that passe, as that a white sheet being displayed unto them by Diego upon the side of a hill, they would carry from me unto him, Bread, flesh, or any other thing I list to send, and upon the like call returne unto mee againe.

Having prevailed thus farre, I began to cast in my head how I might doe to joyne a number of them together in bearing of some great burthen: which if I could bring to passe, I might enable a man to fly and be carried in the ayre, to some certaine place safe and without hurt. In this cogitation having much laboured my wits, and made some triall, I found by experience, that if many were put to the bearing of one great burthen, by reason it was not possible all of them should rise together just in one instant, the first that raised himselfe upon his wings finding himselfe stayed by a weight heavier than hee could move or stirre, would by and by give over, as also would the second, third, and all the rest. I devised (therefore) at last a meanes how each of them might rise carrying but his owne proportion of weight only, and it was thus.

I fastned about every one of my Gansas a little pulley of Corke, and putting a string through it of meetly length, I fastened the one end thereof unto a blocke almost of eight Pound weight, unto the other end of the string I tied a poyse weighing some two Pound, which being done, and causing the signall to be erected, they presently rose all (being 4 in number), and carried away my blocke unto the place appointed. This falling out according to my hope and desire, I made proofe afterwards, but using the help of 2 or 3 birds more, in carrying a Lamb, whose happinesse I much envied, that he should be the first living creature to take possession of such a device.

At last after divers tryalls I was surprized with a great longing, to cause my selfe to be carried in the like sort. Diego my Moore was likewise possessed with the same desire, and but that otherwise I loved him well, and had need of his helpe, I should have resented his ambitious Thought: for I hold it farre more honour to have been the first flying man, than to bee another Neptune that first adventured to sayle upon the Sea. Howbeit not seeming to understand his Intention, I onely told him (which I also take to be true) that all my Gansas were not of sufficient strength to carry him, being a man, though of no great stature, yet twice my weight at least. So upon a time having provided all things necessary, I placed my selfe with all my trinckets, upon the top of a rocke at the River's mouth, and putting my selfe at full Sea upon an Engine (the description whereof ensueth) I caused Diego to advance his signall: whereupon my Birds presently arose, 25 in number, and carried mee over lustily to the other rocke on the other side, being about a Quarter of a league.

The reason why I chose that time and place, was that I thought somewhat might perchance fall out in this enterprise contrary to my expectation, in which case I assured my selfe the worst that could bee, was but to fall into the water, where being able to swim well, I hoped to receive little or no hurt in my fal. But when I was once over in safety, O how did my heart even swell with joy and admiration of mine owne invention! How often did I wish my selfe in the midst of Spaine, that speedily I might fill the world with the fame of my glory and renowne! Every hower wished I with great longing for the Indian Fleet to take mee home with them, but they stayed (by what mischance I know not) 3 Moneths beyond the accustomed time.

At last they came, being in number 3 Carickes sore weather-beaten, their people being for the most part sick and exceeding weak, so as they were constrained to refresh themselves in our Island one whole moneth.

The Admirall was called Alphonso de Xima, a Valiant man, wise, and desirous of renowne, and worthy better fortune then afterward befell him. Unto him I opened the device of my Gansas, well knowing how impossible it were otherwise to perswade him to take in so many Birds into the Ship, that would be more troublesome (for the niceness of provision to be made for them), then so many men; Yet I adjured him by all manner of Oaths, and perswasions, to afford mee both true dealing, and secrecy. Of the last I doubted not much, as assuring my selfe, he would not dare to impart the device to any other, before our King were acquainted with it. Of the first I feared much more, namely, lest Ambition, and the desire of drawing unto himselfe the honour of such an invention, should cause him to make mee away; yet I was forced to run the hazard, except I would adventure the losse of my Birds, the like whereof for my purpose were not to be had in all Christendome, nor any that I could be sure, would ever serve the turne.

Well, that doubt in proofe was causelesse: the man I thinke was honest of himselfe: but had he dealt treacherously with me, I had laid a plot for the discovery of him, as he might easily judge I would, which peradventure somewhat moved him, yet God knowes how he might have used me, before my arrivall in Spaine, if in the meane course wee had not beene intercepted, as you shall heare. Upon Thursday the 21 of June, to wit in the yeare 1599, wee set saile towards Spaine, I having allowed me a very convenient Cabin for my Birds, and stowage also for mine Engine, which the Captaine would have had me leave behinde me, and it is a mervaile I had not, but my good fortune therein saved my life, and gave me that which I esteeme more than an hundred lives, if I had them: for thus it fell out, after 2 moneths saile, we encountered with a fleet of the English, some 10 leagues from the Island of Teneriff, one of the Canaries, which is famous through the World, for a Hill upon the same called el Pico, that is to be discerned and kenned upon the Sea no lesse then 100 leagues off. We had aboord us 5 times the number of people that they had; we were well provided of munition, and our men in good health. Yet seeing them disposed to fight, and knowing what infinite riches wee carried with us, we thought it a wiser way to fly, if we might, then by encountering a company of dangerous fellowes to hazard not onely our owne lives, (which a man of valour in such a case esteemeth not) but the estates of many poore Merchants, who I am affraid were utterly undone by miscarriage of this businesse. Our fleete then consisted of 5 sayle, to wit, 3 Carickes, a Barke, and a Caravell, that comming from the Isle of Saint Thomas, had (in an evill houre for him) overtaken us some few dayes before.

The English had 3 Ships very well appointed, and no sooner spied, but they began to play for us, and changing their course, as wee might well perceive, endeavoured straight way to bring us under their lee, which they might well doe (as the wind stood) especially being light nimble vessells, as for the most part all the English shipping is, whereas ours was heavy, deepe laden, foule with the Sea: our Captaine therefore resolved peradventure wisely enough (but I am sure neither valiantly, nor fortunately) to flie, commanding us to disperse our selves: the Caravell by reason of too much haste fell foule upon one of the Carickes, and bruised her so, that the English easily fetcht her up and entered her: as for the caravell shee sanke immediately in the sight of us all. The Barke (for ought I could perceive) no man making after her, escaped unpursued; and another of our carickes after some chase, was given over by the English, that making account to finde a booty good enough of us, and having us betweene them and their third companion, made upon us with might and maine. Wherefore our Captaine that was aboord us, gave direction to runne ashore upon Teneriff, the Port whereof we could not recover, saying that hee hoped to save

11

some of the goods, and some of our lives, and the rest he had rather should bee lost, then commit all to the mercy of the enemie.

When I heard of that resolution, seeing the Sea to worke high, and knowing all the coast to bee full of blind Rockes, and Shoales, so as our Vessell might not possibly come neere land, before it must needs be rent in a thousand peeces, I went unto the Captaine, shewing him the desperatenesse of the course hee intended, wishing him rather to trie the mercy of the enemie, then so to cast away himselfe, and so many brave men: but hee would not heare me by any meanes; whereupon discerning it to be high time to shift for my selfe, first, I sought out my Box or little Casket of Jewels, and having put it into my sleeve, I then betooke me to my Gansas, put them upon my Engine, and my selfe upon it, trusting (as indeed it happily fell out) that when the Shippe should split, my Birds, although they wanted their Signall, yet for saving their owne lives (which nature hath taught every living creature to preserve to their power) would make towards the Land; which fell out well (I thanke God), according to mine expectation.

The people of our Ship mervailed about what I went, none of them being acquainted with the use of my Birds, but the Captaine, for Diego was in the Rosaria, the ship that fled away unpursued, (as before I told you): some halfe a league we were from the Land, when our Carick struck upon a Rocke, and split immediately: whereupon I let loose unto my Birds the raines, having first placed my selfe upon the highest of the Decke: and with the shock they all arose, carrying mee fortunately unto the Land, of which you need not doubt I was very joyful, but a pittifull sight it was unto me to behold my friends and acquaintances in that miserable distresse of whom (notwithstanding) many escaped better then they had any reason to hope for. For the English, launching out their cockboates like men of more noble and generous disposition then wee are pleased to esteeme them, taking compassion upon them, used all the diligence they could to helpe such as had many meanes to save themselves from the furie of the waves and that even with their owne danger: amongst many, they tooke up our Captaine, who (as Father

Pacio since told me) having put himselfe into his Cock-boat with 12 others, was induced to yeeld himselfe unto one Captaine Raymund, who carried him together with our Pilote along in their voyage with them, being bound for the East Indies; but it was their hard fate, by a breach of the Sea neere the cape of Buona Esperanca, to be swallowed of the mercilesse Waves, whose fury a little before they had so hardly escaped. The rest of them (as I likewise heard), and they were in all some 26 persons that they tooke into their ship, they set them a land soone after at Cape Verde.

As for my selfe, being now a shore in a Country inhabited for the most part by Spaniards, I reckoned my selfe in safety. Howbeit I quickly found myself mistaken; for it was my chance to pitch upon that part of the Isle where the hill, before mentioned, beginneth to rise. And it is inhabited by a Savage kinde of people, that live upon the sides of that hill, the top whereof is alwayes covered with Snow, and held for the monstrous height and steepnesse not to be accessible either for man or beast. Howbeit these Savages fearing the Spaniards, (betweene whom and them there is a kinde of continuall warre) hold themselves as neere the top of that hill as they can, where they have divers places of good strength, never comming downe into the fruitfull Valleys, but to prey upon what they can finde there. It was the chance of a company of them to espie mee within some howers space after my Landing: They thinking they had light upon a booty, made towards mee with all the speed they could, but not so privily as that I could not perceive their purpose before they came neere to me by halfe a Quarter of a League; seeing them come down the side of a Hill with great speed directly towards mee, divers of them carrying Long Staves, besides other weapons, which because of their distance from mee I might not discerne. I thought it high time to bestirre mee, and shift for my selfe, and by all meanes, to keepe my selfe out of the fingers of such slaves, who had they caught mee, for the hatred they beare to us Spaniards, had surely hewed mee all to peeces.

The Country in that place was bare, without the coverture of any wood: But the mountaine before spoken of, beginning even there to lift up itselfe, I espied in the side of the same a white

13

cliffe, which I trusted my Gansas would take for a signall, and being put off, would make all that way, whereby I might quickly bee carried so farre, as those barbarous Rascals should not be able to overtake mee, before I had recovered to the dwelling of some Spaniard, or at least-wise might have time to hide my selfe from them, till that in the night, by helpe of the starres, I might guide my selfe toward Las Laeguna, the City of that Island, which was about one league off, as I thinke. Wherefore with all the celeritie that might be I put my selfe upon mine Engine, and let loose the raines unto my Gansas. It was my good fortune that they tooke all one way, although not just that way I aymed at. But what then, O Reader? Prick up thy Ears, prepare thy selfe unto the hearing of the strangest Chance that ever happened to any mortall man, and that I know thou wilt not have the Grace to beleeve, till thou seest the like Experiment, which I doubt not in a short Time may be performed. My Gansas, like so many horses that had gotten the bitt betweene their teeth, made (I say) not towards the cliffe I aymed at, although I used my wonted meanes to direct the Leader of the flocke that way, but with might and maine tooke up towards the top of El Pico, and did never stay till they came there, a place where they say never man came before, being in all estimation at least 15 leagues in height perpendicularly upward, above the ordinary levell of the Land and Sea.

What manner of place I found there, I should gladly relate unto you, but that I make haste to matters of farre greater Importance. There when I set downe, I saw my poore Gansas, fall to panting and blowing, gaping for breath, as if they would all presently have died: wherefore I thought it not good to trouble them a while, forbearing to draw them in, (which they never wont to indure without struggling) and little expecting that which followed.

It was now the season that these Birds were wont to take their flight away, as our Cuckoes and swallowes doe in Spaine, towards the Autumne. They (as after I perceived) mindfull of their usuall voyage, even as I began to settle my selfe for the taking of them in, as it were with one consent, rose up, and having no other place higher to make toward, to my unspeakable feare and amazement struck bolt upright, and never left towring upward, and still upward, for the space, as I might guesse, of one whole hower; toward the end of which time, mee thought I might perceive them to labour lesse and lesse; till at length, O incredible thing! they forbare moving anything at all and yet remained unmoveable, as steadfastly, as if they had beene upon so many perches; the Lines slacked; neither I, nor the Engine moved at all, but abode still as having no manner of weight.

I found then by this Experience that which no Philosopher ever dreamed of, to wit, that those things which wee call heavie, do not sinke toward the Center of the Earth, as their naturall place, but are drawn by a secret property of the Globe of the Earth, or rather some thing within the same, in like sort as the Loadstone draweth Iron, being within the compasse of its attractive beames.

For though it bee true that there my gansas could abide unmoved without the proppe or sustentation of any corporall thing other then the ayre, as easily and quietly as a fish in the middle of the water, yet forcing themselves never so little, it is not possible to imagine with what swiftnesse and celeritie they were carried, and whether it were upward, downward, or sidelong, all was one. Truly I must confesse, the horror and amazement of that place was such, as if I had not been armed with a true Spanish courage and resolution, I must needs have died there with very feare.

But the next thing that did most trouble me, was the swiftnesse of Motion, such as did even almost stop my breath; If I should liken it to an Arrow out of a Bow, or to a stone cast downe from the top of some high tower, it would come vastly short of it.

Another thing there was exceeding, and more than exceeding, troublesome unto mee, and that was the Illusions of Devills and wicked spirits, who, the first day of my arrivall, came about mee in great numbers, carrying the shapes and likenesse of men and women, wondring at mee like so many Birds about an Owle, and speaking divers kindes of Languages: which I understood not, till at last I did light upon them that spake very good

Spanish, some Dutch, and others Italian, for all these Languages I understood.

And here I saw onely a touch of the Sunnes absence for a little while once, ever after having him in my sight. Now to yeeld you satisfaction in the other, you shall understand that my Gansas, although entangled in my lynes, might easily find means to sease upon divers kinds of flyes and Birds, as especially Swallowes, and Cuckoes, whereof there were multitudes, as Motes in the sunne; although to say the truth I never saw them to feed any thing at all. As for my selfe, in truth I was much beholding unto those same, whether men or Divels I know not, that amongst divers speeches, which I will forbeare a while to relate, told me, that if I would follow their directions, I should not onely bee brought safely to my home, but also be assured to have the command of all pleasures of that place, at all times.

To the which motions not daring to make a flat deniall, I prayed a time to thinke of it, and withall intreated them (though I felt no hunger at all, which may seeme strange) to helpe mee with some victualls, least in the meane while I should starve. They did so, readily enough, and brought me very good Flesh, and Fish, of divers sorts well dressed, but that it was exceeding fresh, and without any manner of relish of salt. Wine also I tasted there of divers sorts, as good as any in Spayne, and Beere, no better in all Antwerp. They advised me, while I had meanes to make my provision, telling me, that till the next Thursday they could not helpe me to any more, at what time they would find meanes to carry me backe and set mee safe in Spayne where I would wish to be, so that I would become one of their fraternity, and enter into such covenants and profession as they had made to their Master and Captaine, whom they would not name. I answered them gently for the time, telling them, I saw little reason to be very glad of such an offer, praying them to be mindfull of me as occasion served. So for that time I was ridd of them, having first furnished my Pocketts with as much Victuall as I could thrust in, amongst the which I failed not to afford place for a little Bottle of good Canary wine.

Now I shall declare unto you the quality of the place, in which I then was. The Clouds I perceived to be all under me, betweene mee and the earth. The starres, by reason it was alwaies day, I saw at all times alike, not shining bright, as upon the earth we are wont to see them in the night time; but of a whitish Colour, like that of the Moone in the day time with us: And such of them as were to be seene (which were not many) I shewed farre greater then with us, yea (as I should guesse) no lesse then ten times so great. As for the Moone being then within two daies of the change, she appeared of a huge and fear-full quantitie.

This also is not to be forgotten, that no starres appeared but on that part of the Hemispheare that was next the Moone, and the neerer to her the bigger in Quantity they shewed. Againe I must tell you, that whether I lay quiet and rested, or else were carried in the Ayre, I perceived my selfe still to be alwaies directly betweene the Moone and the earth. Whereby it appeareth, not only that my Gansas took none other way than directly toward the Moone, but also, that when we rested (as at first we did for many howers), either we were insensibly carryed, (for I percieved no such motion) round the Globe of the Earth, or else that (according to the late opinion of Copernicus), the Earth is carried about, and turneth round perpetually, from West to the East, leaving unto the Planets onely that motion which Astronomers call naturall, and is not upon the Poles of the Equinoctiall, commonly termed the Poles of the World, but upon those of the Zodiake; concerning which question, I will speake more hereafter, when I shall have leysure to call to my remembrance the Astronomy that I learned being a young man at Salamanca, but have now almost forgotten.

The ayre in that place I found quiet without any motion of wind, and exceeding temperate, neither hot nor cold, where neither the Sunne-beames had any subject to reflect upon, neither was yet either the earth or water so neere as to affect the ayre with their naturall quality of coldnesse. As for that imagina-tion of the Philosophers, attributing heat together with moyst-nesse unto the ayre, I never esteemed it otherwise then a fancy. Lastly now it is to be remembred that after my departure from the earth, I never felt any appetite of hunger or thirst. Whether the purity of the Ayre our proper element not being infected with any Vapors of the Earth and water might yeeld nature sufficient nutriment; or what else might be the cause of it, I cannot tell but so I found it, although I perceived my selfe in perfect health of body, having the use of all my Limmes and senses; and strength both of body and minde, even above my usual Vigour.

Not many howers after the departure of that devilish company from me, my Gansas began to bestir themselves, still directing their course toward the Globe or body of the Moone: And they made their way with that incredible swiftnesse, as I thinke they gained not so little as Fifty Leagues in every hower. In that passage I noted three things very remarkeable: one that the further we went, the lesser the Globe of the Earth appeared unto us; whereas the Moone shewed her selfe more and more monstrously huge.

Againe, the Earth (which ever I held in mine eye) did as it were mask itselfe with a kinde of brightnesse like another Moone; and even as in the Moone we discerned certaine spots or Clouds, as it were, so did I then in the earth. But whereas the forme of those spots in the Moone continue constantly one and the same; these little and little did change every hower. The reason thereof I conceive to be this, that whereas the Earth according to her naturall motion, (for that such a motion she hath, I am now constrained to joyne in opinion with Copernicus), turneth round upon her owne Axe every 24 howers from the West unto the East: I should at the first see in the middle of the body of this new starre a spot like unto a Peare that had a morsell bitten out upon the one side of him; after certaine howers, I should see that spot slide away to the East side. This no doubt was the maine of Africa. Then should I perceive a great shining brightnesse to occupy that roome, during the like time (which was undoubtedly none other then the great Atlantick Ocean). After that succeeded a spot almost of an Ovall form, even just such as we see America to have in our Mapps. Then another vast cleernesse representing the West Ocean; and lastly a medly of spots, like the Countries of the East Indies. So that it seemed unto me no other then a huge Mathematicall Globe, leasurely turned before me, wherein successively, all the Countries of our earthly world within the compasse of 24 howers were represented to my sight. And this was all the meanes I had now to number the dayes, and take reckoning of time.

Philosophers and Mathematicians I would should now confesse the wilfulnesse of their owne blindnesse. They have made the world beleeve hitherto, that the Earth hath no motion. And to make that good they are fain to attribute unto all and every of the celestial bodies, two motions quite contrary each to other; whereof one is from the East to the West, to be performed in 24 howers; (that they imagine to be forced, with an impetuous rapid motion) the other from the West to the East in severall proportions.

O incredible thing, that those same huge bodies of the fixed stars in the highest orbe, whereof divers are by themselves confessed to be more then one hundreth times as bigge as the whole earth, should as so many nayles in a Cart Wheele, be whirled about in that short space, whereas it is many thousands of Years (no lesse, I trowe, they say, then 30 thousand) before that orb do finish his Course from West to East, which they call the naturall motion. Now whereas to every of these they yeeld their naturall course from West to East; therein they doe well. The Moone performeth it in 27 daies; the Sunne, Venus, and Mercury in a Yeare or thereabouts, Mars in three Yeare, Jupiter in twelve Yeares, and Saturne in 30. But to attribute unto these celestiall bodies contrary motions at once, was a very absurd conceit, and much more, to imagine that same Orbe wherein the fixed stars are, (whose naturall course taketh so many thousand of yeares) should every 24 howers be turned about. I will not go so farre as Copernicus, that maketh the Sunne the Center of the Earth, and unmoveable, neither will I be positive in any thing, only this I say, allow the Earth his motion (which these eyes of mine can testifie to be true) and these absurdities are quite taken away, every one having his single and proper Motion onely.

But where am I? At the first I promised an History, and I fall into disputes before I am aware. There is yet one accident more befell me worthy of especiall remembrance: that during the time of my stay I saw as it were a kind of cloud of a reddish colour growing toward me, which continually growing nearer and nearer, at last I perceived to be nothing else but a huge swarme of Locusts. He that readeth the discourses of learned men, concerning them; and namely that of Iohn Leo, in his description of Africa, how that they are seene in the Ayre many dayes before they fall upon a countrey, and adds thereto this experience of mine, will easily conclude, that they cannot come from any other place then the Globe of the Moone.

But give me leave now at last to passe on my journey quietly, without interruption for Eleven or Twelve daies, during all which time, I was carried directly toward the Globe or body of the Moone with such a violent whirling as cannot bee expressed. For I cannot imagine that a bullet out of the mouth of a Cannon could make way through the vaporous and muddie aire neere the earth with that celerity, which is most strange, considering that my Gansas moved their wings but even now and then, and sometimes not at all in a Quarter of an hower together; only they held them stretched out, so passing on, as we see that Eagles, and Kites sometimes will doe for a little space, and during the time of those pauses I beleeve they tooke their napps and times of sleeping; for other (as I might easily note) they had none.

Now for my selfe, I was so fast knit unto my Engin, as I durst commit my selfe to slumbring enough to serve my turne, which I tooke with as great ease (although I am loath to speake it, because it may seeme incredible) as if I had beene in the best Bed of downe in all Antwerp.

After Eleven daies passage in this violent flight, I perceived that we began to approach neare unto another Earth, if I may so call it, being the Globe or very body of that starre which we call the Moone.

The first difference that I found betweene it and our earth, was, that it shewed it selfe in his naturall colours: as soon as I was free from the attraction of the Earth; whereas with us, a thing removed from our eye but a league or two, begins to put on that lurid and deadly colour of blue.

Then, I perceived also, that it was covered for the most part with a huge and mighty Sea, those parts only being drie Land, which shew unto us here somewhat darker then the rest of her body that I mean which the Country people cal *el hombre della Luna*, the Man in the Moone. As for that part which shineth so clearly in our eyes; it is even another Ocean, yet besprinckled heere and there with Islands, which for the littlenesse, so farre off we cannot discern. So that same splendor appearing unto us, and giving light unto our night, appeareth to be nothing else but the reflexion of the Sun beames returned unto us out of the water, as out of a glasse: How ill this agreeth with that which our Philosophers teach in the schooles I am not ignorant.

But alas how many of their Errors hath time and experience refuted in this our age, with the recitall whereof I will not stand to trouble the reader. Amongst many other of their vaine surmises, the time and order of my narration putteth me in mind of one which now my experience found most untrue. Who is there that hath not hitherto beleeved the uppermost Region of the Ayre to be extreame hot, as being next forsooth unto the naturall place of the Element of Fire. O Vanities, fansies, Dreames!

After the time I was once quite free from the attractive Beames of that tyrannous Loadstone the earth, I found the ayre of one and the selfe same temper, without Winds, without Raine, without Mists, without Clouds, neither hot nor cold, but continually after one and the same tenor, most pleasant, milde, and comfortable, till my arrivall in that new World of the Moone. As for that Region of Fire our Philosophers talke of, I heard no newes of it; mine eyes have sufficiently informed me there can be no such thing.

The Earth by turning about had now shewed me all her parts twelve times when I finished my course: For when by my reckoning it seemed to be (as indeed it was) Tuesday the Eleventh day of September, (at what time the Moone being two daies old was in the Twentieth degree of Libra), my Gansas staied their course as it was with one consent, and tooke their rest, for certaine howers; after which they tooke their flight, and within lesse then one hower, set me upon the top of a very high hill in that other world, where immediately were presented unto mine eyes many most strange and unwonted sights.

For first I observed, that although the Globe of the Earth shewed much bigger there then the Moone doth unto us, even to the full trebling of her diameter, yet all manner of things there were of largenesse and quantity, 10, 20, I thinke I may say 30 times more then ours. Their trees were at least three times so high as ours, and more then five times the breadth and thicknesse. So were their herbes, Beasts, and Birds; although to compare them with ours I know not well how, because I found not any thing there, any species either of Beast or Bird that resembled ours any thing at all, except Swallowes, Nightingales, Cuckooes, Woodcockes, Batts, and some kindes of wild Fowle, as also of such Birds as my Gansas, all which, (as now I well perceived,) spend the time of their absence from us, even there in that world; neither do they vary any thing at all either in quantity or quality from those of ours heere, as being none other then the very same.

No sooner was I set downe upon the ground, but I was surprised with a most ravenous hunger, and earnest desire of eating. Wherefore stepping unto the next tree, I fastened thereunto my engine, with my Gansas, and in great haste fell to searching of my pockets for the Victuals I had reserved as aforesaid: but to my great amazement and discomfort, I found in stead of Partridge, and Capon which I thought to have put there, a mingle mangle of drye leaves, of Goats hayre, sheepe, or Goats-dung, Mosse, and such like trash. As for my Canary Wine, it was turned to a stinking and filthie kind of liquor like the Urine of some Beast. O the illusions of wicked spirits, whose helpe if I had beene faine only to rely upon, you see how I had beene served.

Now while I stood musing and wondering at this strange Metamorphosis, I heard my Gansas upon the sudden to make a great fluttering behind me. And looking back, I espied them to fall greedily upon a certaine shrub within the compasse of their lines, whose leaves they fed upon most earnestly; where heretofore, I had never seene them to eat any manner of greene thing whatsoever. Whereupon stepping to the shrub, I put a leafe of it between my teeth: I cannot expresse the pleasure I found in the taste thereof; such it was I am sure, as if I had not with great discretion moderated my appetite, I had surely surfetted upon the same. In the meane time it fell out to be a baite that well contented both my Birds and me at that time when we had need, of some good refreshing.

Scarcely had I ended this banquett, when upon the sudden I saw my selfe environed with a kind of people most strange, both for their feature, demeanure, and apparell. Their stature was most divers but for the most part, twice the height of ours: their colour and countenance most pleasing, and their habit such, as I know not how to expresse. For neither did I see any kind of Cloth, Silke, or other stuffe to resemble the matter of that whereof their Clothes were made; neither (which is most strange, of all other) can I devise how to describe the colour of them, being in a manner all clothed alike. It was neither blacke, nor white, yellow, nor redd, greene nor blue, nor any colour composed of these. But if you aske me what it was then; I must tell you, it was a colour never seene in our earthly world, and therefore neither to be described unto us by any, nor to be conceived of one that never saw it. For as it were a hard matter to describe unto a man borne blind the difference betweene blue and Greene, so can I not bethinke my selfe any meane how to decipher unto you this Lunar colour, having no affinitie with any other that ever I beheld with mine eyes. Onely this I can say of it, that it was the most glorious and delightfull that can possibly be imagined; neither in truth was there any one thing, that more delighted me, during my abode in that new world, than the beholding of that most pleasing and resplendent colour.

It remaineth now that I speake of the Demeanure of this people, who presenting themselves unto me upon the sudden and that in such extraordinary fashion as I have declared; being struck with a great amasement, I crossed my selfe, and cried out, Iesus Maria.

No sooner was the word Iesus out of my mouth, but young and old, fell all downe upon their knees, (at which I not a little rejoyced) holding up both their hands on high, and repeating all certaine words which I understood not. Then presently they all arising, one that was farre the tallest of them came unto me, and embraced me, with great kindnesse, and giving order (as I partly perceived) unto some of the rest to stay by my Birds, he tooke me by the hand, and leading me downe toward the foote of the hill, brought me to his dwelling, being more then half a league from the place where I first alighted.

It was such a building for beauty and hugenesse, as all our world cannot shew any neere comparable to it. Yet such I saw afterwards elsewhere, as this might seeme but a Cottage in respect of them. There was not a doore about the house, that was not 30 foote high, and twelve in breadth. The roomes were betweene 40 and 50 foote in height, and so all other proportions answerable. Neither could they well be much lesse, the Master inhabiting them, being full 28 high. As for his corporature, I suppose verily that if we had him here in this world to be weighed in the ballance, the poyse of his body would shew it selfe more ponderous then Five and Twenty, peradventure thirty of ours.

After I had rested my selfe with him the Value of one of our dayes; he ledd me some Five leagues off, unto the Palace of the Prince of the Country. The statelinesse of the building whereof I will leave unto the second part of this worke, as also many other particulars, which will minister more pleasure to the reader, then yet I may affoord him, being desirous in this first part to set down no more than what the processe of my story concerning my Iourney doth necessarily draw from me.

This Prince whose stature was much higher then the former, is called (as neere as I can by Letters declare it, for their sounds are not perfectly to be expressed by our Characters) Pylonas, which signifieth in their Language, First, if perhaps it be not rather a denotation of his dignity and authority, as being the prime Man in all those parts.

In all those parts, I say. For there is one supreme Monarch amongst them, of stature yet much more huge then hee, commanding over all that whole Orbe of that world, having under him 29 other Princes of exceeding great power, and every of them 24 others, whereof this Pylonas was one. The first ancestor of this great Monarch came out of the earth (as they relate) and by marriage with the Heiress of that huge Monarchy, obtaining the government, left it unto his posteritie, who ever since have held the same, even for the space of 40 thousand daies or Moones, which amounteth unto 3077 Yeeres.

And his name being Irdonozur, his heires, unto this day, doe all assume unto themselves that name, hee, they say, having continued there well neere 400 Moones, and having begotten divers children, returned (by what meanes they declare not) unto the Earth againe: I doubt not but they may have their Fables, as well as we. And because our Histories afford no mention of any earthly man to have ever beene in that world before my selfe, and much lesse to have returned thence againe, I cannot but condemne that tradition as false and fabulous; yet this I must tell you, that learning seemeth to be in great estimation among them: And that they make semblance of detesting all Lying and falshood, which is wont there to be severely punished and which which may yeeld some Credit unto their historicall narrations.

Many of them live wonderfull long; even beyond Belief to wit even unto the age as they professed unto mee of 30,000 Moones, which amounteth unto 1,000 Yeares and Upwards, (so that the ages of 3 or 4 men might well reach unto the time of the first Irdonozur), and this is noted generally, that the taller people are of Stature, the more excellent they are for all indowments of mind, and the longer time they doe live. For whereas (that which before I partly intimated unto you) their stature is most divers, great numbers of them little exceeding ours; such seldome live above a 1,000 moones, which is answerable to 80 of our Yeares, and they account them most base creatures, even but a degree before bruite beasts, imploying them accordingly in all the beast and most servile offices, calling them by a word that signifieth bastard-men, counterfetts, or Changelings; so those whom they account Genuine, naturall, and true Lunars, both in quantitie of bodie, and length of life, exceed ours generally 30 times, which proportion agreeeth well with the quantitie of the day in both worlds, theirs containing almost 30 of ours.

Now when shall I declare unto you the manner of our travell unto the Palace of Pylonas, you will say you scarce ever heard any thing more strange and incredible. Unto every one of us there was delivered at our first setting forth, two Fans of Feathers, not much unlike to those that our Ladies doe carrie in Spaine, to make a coole Ayre unto themselves in the heat of Summer. The use of which Fans before I declare unto you, I must let you understand that the Globe of the Moone is not altogether destitute of an attractive Power: but it is so farre weaker than that ot the earth, as if a man doe but spring upward, with all his force, (as Dancers doe when they shew their activity by capering) he shall be able to mount 50 or 60 foote high, and then he is quite beyond all attraction of the Moones earth, falling downe no more, so as by the helpe of these Fans, as with wings, they conveigh themselves in the Ayre in a short space (although not with that swiftnesse that Birds doe) whither they please.

In two howers time (as I could guesse) by the helpe of these fans, wee were carried through the Ayre those five Leagues, being about 60 persons. Being arrived at the Palace of Pylonas, after our conductor had gotten audience and had declared what manner of present he had brought; I was called in unto him by his attendants. By the statelinesse of his Palace, and the reverence done unto him, I soone discerned his greatnesse, and therefore framed my selfe to win his favour the best I might. You may remember I told you of a certaine little Box or Caskett of Jewels, the remainder of those brought out of the East Indies. These before I was carried in unto him I tooke out my pockett, and making choice of some of every sort, made them ready to be presented as I should think fit.

I found him sitting in a most magnificent chaire of State, having his Wife or Queene upon one hand, and his eldest sonne on the other, which both were attended, the one by a troupe of Ladies, and the other of young men, and all along the side of the roome stood a great number of goodly personages, whereof scarce any one was lower of stature then Pylonas, whose age they say is now 21,000 moones. At my first entrance falling downe upon my knees, I thought good to use unto him these words in the Latine tongue, *Propitius sit tibi Princeps Illustrissime Dominus noster Jesus Christus &c.* As the people I first met withall, so they hearing the holy name of our Saviour, they all, I say, King, Queene, and all the rest fell downe upon their knees, pronouncing a word or two I understood not. They being risen againe I proceeded thus, *& Maria Salvatoris Genetrix, Petrus & Paulus &c.* and so reckoning up a number of Saints, to see if there were any one of them that they honoured as their patron, at last reckoning among others St. Martinus, they all bowed their bodies, and held up hands in signe of great reverence: the reason whereof I learned to bee, that Martin in their language signifieth God: Then taking out my Jewells, prepared for that purpose, I presented unto the King or Prince (call him how you please) 7 stones of so many severall sorts, a Diamond, a Rubie, an Emerauld, a Saphire, a Topaze, a Turquez, and an Opall, which he accepted with great joy and admiration, as having not often seene any such before.

Then I offered unto the Queene and Prince some other, and was about to have bestowed a number of more, upon other there present, but Pylonas forbade them to accept, thinking (as afterwards I learned) that they were all I had, and being willing they should be reserved for Irdonozur his Soveraigne.

This done he imbraced me with great kindnesse, and began to inquire of me divers things by signes, which I likewise answered by signes as well as I could. But not contenting him, he delivered me to a guard of a 100 of his Giants (so I may wel call them) commanding straightly, First that I should want nothing that might be fit for mee; Secondly that they should not suffer any of the dwarfe Lunars (if I may so tearme them) to come neere mee; Thirdly that I should with all diligence to be instructed in their Language. And lastly, that by no meanes should they impart unto me the knowledge of certaine things, particularly by him specified, though what those particulars were, I could never understand.

It may bee now you will desire to understand what were the things Pylonas inquired of mee. Why what but these? whence I came, how I arrived there, and by what meanes? what was my name? what my Errand, and such like? To all which I answered the very truth as neere as I could.

Being dismissed, I was affoorded all manner of necessaries that my heart could wish, so as it seemed unto me I was in a very Paradise, the pleasures whereof notwithstanding could not so overcome mee, as that the remembrance of my wife and Children, did not trouble mee much. And therefore being willing to foster any small sparke of hope of my returne, with great diligence I tooke order for the attendance of my Gansas whom my selfe in person tended every day with great carefulnesse; All which notwithstanding had fallen out to little purpose, had not other mens care peformed that which no indeavour of mine owne could. For the time now approached, when of necessity all the people of our stature, (and so my selfe among the rest) must needes sleepe for some 13 or 14 whole dayes together.

So it commeth to passe there by a secret power, and unresistable decree of nature, that when the day beginneth to appeare, and the Moone to bee enlightened by the Sunne beames, (which is at the first Quarter of the Moon) all such people as exceed not very much our stature inhabiting those parts, they fall into a dead sleepe, and are not possibly to be wakened till the Sun be sett, and withdrawne out of their sight, even as Owles, and Batts, with us cannot indure the light, so wee there at the first approach of the day, begin to be amazed with it, and fall immediately into a slumber, which groweth by little and little, into a dead sleepe, till this light depart from thence againe, which is not in 14 or 15 daies, to wit, untill the last quarter.

Mee thinkes now I heare some man to demand what manner of light there is in that world during the absence of the Sunne, to resolve you for that point, you shall understand that there is a light of two sorts. One of the Sun (which I might not endure to behold), and another of the Earth: that of the Earth was now at the highest; for that when the Moone is at the Change, then is the Earth (unto them in the Moon) like a full Moone with us, and as the Moone increaseth with us; so the light of the Earth decreaseth with them: I then found the light there (though the Sunne were absent) equall unto that with us, in the day time, when the Sun is covered with clouds, but toward the quarter it little and little diminisheth, yet leaving still a competent light, which is somewhat strange.

But much stranger is that which was reported unto me there, how that in the other Hemispheare of the Moone (I meane contrary to that I happened upon), where during halfe the Moone, they see not the sunne, and the Earth never appeareth unto them, they have notwithstanding a kinde of light (not unlike by their description to our Moon light) which it seemeth the propinquitie of the starres and other Planets (so much neerer unto them then us) affoordeth.

Now you shall understand that of the true Lunars there bee three degrees. Some a little taller than we, as perhaps 10 or 12 foote high, that can indure the day of the Moone, when the earth shineth but little, but not endure the beames of both; at such time they must be content to bee laid asleepe. Others are of 20 foote high, or somewhat more, that in ordinary places indure all light both of earth & Sun. There are in a certaine Island, the mysteries whereof none may know, men whose stature is at least 27 foot high (I meane of the measure of the Standard of Castile). If any other come aland there in the Moones day time, they fall asleepe immediately: This Island they call Gods Island, or *Insula Martini* in their language: they say it hath a particular governour, who is (as they report) of age 65,000 Moones, which amounteth of 5,000 of our Yeares. His name is said to be Hiruch, and he commandeth after a sort over Irdonozur himselfe, especially in that Island out of which he never commeth.

There is another repairing much thither, they say is halfe his age and upwards, to wit, about 33 thousand Moones, or 26 hundreth of our Yeares, and hee commandeth in all things (throughout the whole Globe of the Moone) concerning matters of Religion, and the service of God, as absolutely as our holy Father the Pope doth in any part of Italy. I would faine have seene this man, but I might not be suffered to come neere him: his name is Imozes.

Now give mee leave to settle my selfe to a long night's sleepe: My attendants take charge of my Birds, prepare my lodging, and signifie to mee by signes, how it must bee with mee. It was about the middle of September, when I perceived the Ayre to grow more cleare then ordinary, and with the increasing of the light, I began to feele my selfe first dull, then heavy and willing to sleepe, although I had not lately been hindred from taking mine ease that way. I delivered my selfe at last into the custody of this sister of Death, whose prisoner I was for almost a fortnight after; Awaking then, it is not to bee beleeved how fresh, how nimble, how vigorous, I found all the faculties both of my bodie and minde.

In good time, therefore, I setled my selfe immediately to the learning of the language which (a marvellous thing to consider) is one of the same throughout all the regions of the Moone, yet so much the lesse to be wondred at, because I cannot thinke all the Earth of Moone to Amount to the fortieth part of our inhabited Earth; partly because the Globe of the Moone is much lesse then that of the Earth, and partly because their Sea or Ocean covereth in estimation Three parts or Foure, (if not more) whereas the superficies of our land may bee judged Equivalent and comparable in Measure to that of our Seas.

The Difficulty of that language is not to bee conceived, and the reasons thereof are especially two: First, because it hath no affinitie with any other that ever I heard. Secondly, because it consisteth not so much of words and Letters, as of tunes and uncouth sounds, that no letters can expresse. For you have few wordes but they signifie divers and severall things, and they are distinguished onely by their tunes that are as it were sung in the utterance of them, yea many wordes there are consisting of tunes onely, so as if they list they will utter their mindes by tunes without wordes: for Example, they have an ordinary salutation amongst them, signifying (*Verbatim*) Glorie be to God alone, which they expresse (as I take it, for I am no perfect Musitian) by this tune without any words at all.

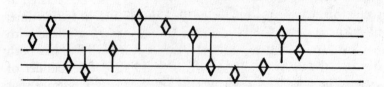

Yea the very names of Men they will expresse in the same sort.
When they were disposed to talke of mee before my face, so as I should not perceive it; this was Gonsales.

By occasion hereof, I discerne meanes of framing a Language (and that easie soone to bee learned) as copious as any other in the world, consisting of tunes onely, whereof my friends may know more at leasure if it please them. This is a great Mystery and worthier the searching after then at first sight you would imagine.

Now notwithstanding the difficulty of this language, within two months space I had attained unto such knowledge of the same, as I could understand most questions to be demanded of mee, and what with signes, what with words, make reasonable shift to utter my mind, which thing being certified unto Pylonas, hee sent for mee oftentimes, and would bee pleased to give mee knowledge of many things that my Guardians durst not declare unto mee. Yet this I will say of them, that they never abused mee with any untruth that I could perceive, but if I asked a question that they liked not to resolve mee in, they would shake their heads and with a Spanish shrugge passe over to other talke.

After 7 moneths time it happened that the great Irdonozur makeing his progresse to a place some 200 leagues distant from the Palace of Pylonas, sent for mee. The History of that Journey, and the conference that passed between us shall bee related at large in my second booke. Onely thus much thereof at this time, that hee would not admit me into his presence, but talked with me through a Window, where I might heare him, and hee both heare and see mee at pleasure. I offered him the remainder of my Jewells, which he accepted very thankfully; telling mee that hee would requite them with gifts of an other manner of value.

It was not above a Quarter of a Moone that I stayed there, before I was sent backe unto Pylonas againe; and so much the sooner, because if we had stayed but a day or two longer, the

Sunne would have overtaken us, before wee could have recovered our home.

The gifts he bestowed on me were such as a Man would forsake mountaines of Gold for, and they were all stones, to wit 9 in number, and those of 3 sorts, whereof one they call Poleastis, another Machrus, and third Ebelus, of each sort three. The first are of the bignesse of an Hazell-nutt, very like unto jett, which among many other incredible vertues hath this property that being once heat in the Fire, they ever after retaine their heat (though without any outward appearance) untill they be quenched with some kinde of liquor, whereby they receive no detriment at all, though they bee heated and quenched a thousand times. And their heat is so vehement, as they will make red hot any mettall that shall come within a foot of them, and being put in a Chimney, will make a roome as warme, as if a great Fire were kindled in the same.

The Machrus (yet farre more precious then the other) is of the colour of Topaze, so shining and resplendent, as (though not past the bignesse of a beane, yet) being placed in the midst of a large Church in the night time, it maketh it all as light, as if a 100 Lamps were hanged up round about it.

Can you wish for properties in a stone of greater use then these. Yet my Ebelus will affoord you that which I dare say will make you preferre him before these, yea and all the Diamonds, Saphyres, Rubies, and Emeralds that our world can yeeld, were they laid in a heap before you; To say nothing of the colour, (the Lunar whereof I made mention before, which notwithstanding is so incredibly beautifull, as a man should travell 1000 Leagues to behold it) the shape is somewhat flat, of the breadth of a Piece of Eight, and twice the thicknesse. One side of this is somewhat more Orient of Colour then the other, which being clapt to the bare skin of a man, in any part of his bodie, it taketh away from it all weight or ponderousnesse; whereas turning the other side it addeth force unto the attractive beames of the Earth, either in this world or that, and maketh the bodie to weigh halfe so much againe as it did before; do you marvell now why I should so overprize this stone? Before you see mee on earth againe, you shall understand more of the value of this kinde and unvaluable Jem.

I inquired then amongst them, whether they had not any kinde of Jewell or other meanes to make a man invisible, which mee thought had beene a thing of great and extraordinary use. And I could mention that divers of our learned men had written many things to that purpose.

They answered that if it were possible, they assured themselves that God would not suffer it to be revealed to us creatures subject to so many imperfections, being a thing so apt to be abused to ill purposes; and that was all I could get of them.

Now after it was known that Irdonozur, the great Monarch, had done me this honour, it is strange how much all men respected mee more then before: my Guardians who hitherto were very cautious in relating any thing to mee, concerning the government of that world, now became somewhat more open, so as I could learne (partly of them and partly of Pylonas), what I shall deliver unto you concerning that matter, whereof I will onely give you a taste at this time: referring you unto a more ample discourse in my second part, which at my returne into Spaine you shall have at large; but not till then for causes heretofore related.

In a thousand yeares it is not found that there is either Thief nor Whoremonger amongst them, whereof these reasons are to bee yeelded: There is no want of any thing necessary for the use of man. Food groweth every where without labour, and that of all sorts to be desired. For rayment, howsing, or any thing else that you may imagine possible for a man to want, or desire, it is provided by the command of Superiors, though not without labour, yet so little, as they doe nothing but as it were playing, and with pleasure.

Againe their Females are all of an absolute beauty: and I know not how it commeth to passe by a secret disposition of nature there, that a man having once knowne a Woman, never desireth any other. As for murther it was never heard of amongst them; neither is it a thing almost possible to bee committed: for there is no wound to bee given which may not bee cured, they assured mee, (and I for my part doe beleeve it), that although a mans head be cut off, yet if any time within the space of Three Moones it bee put together, and joyned to the Carkasse againe, with the appointment of the Juice of a certaine hearbe, there growing, it will be joyned together againe, so as the partie wounded shall become perfectly whole in a few houres.

But the chiefe cause, is that through an excellent disposition of that nature of people there, all, young and old, doe hate all manner of vice, and doe live in such love, peace, amd amitie, as it seemeth to bee another Paradise. True it is, that some are better disposed than others: but that they discerne immediately at the time of their birth. And because it is an inviolable decree amongst them, never to put any one to death, peceiving by the stature, and some other notes they have, who are likely to bee of a wicked or imperfect disposition, they send them away (I know not by what meanes) into the Earth, and change them for other children, before they shall have either abilitie or opportunitie to doe amisse among them: But first (they say) they are faine to keepe them there for a certaine time, till that the ayre of the Earth may alter their colour to be like unto ours.

And their ordinary vent for them is a certaine high hill in the North of America, whose people I can easily beleeve to be wholly descended of them, partly in regard of their colour, partly also in regard of the continuall use of Tobacco which the Lunars use exceeding much, as living in a place abounding wonderfully with moysture, as also for the pleasure they take in it, and partly in some other respects too long now to be rehearsed. Sometimes they mistake their aime, and fall upon Christendome, Asia or Africa, marry that is but seldome: I remember some yeares since, that I read certaine stories tending to the confirmation of these things delivered by these Lunars, as especially one Chapter of Guil. Neubrigensis, *de reb. Angl.*: it is towards the end of his first booke, but the chapter I cannot particularly resigne.

Then see Jnigo Mondejar in his description of *Nueva Granata*, the second booke; as also Ioseph Desia de Carana, in his history of Mexico: if my memory faile mee not, you will find that in these, which will make my report much the more credible: But for testimonies I care not.

May I once have the happinesse to returne home in safety, I will yeeld such demonstrations of all I deliver, as shall quickly make void all doubt of the truth hereof.

If you will aske mee further of the manner of government amongst the Lunars, and how Justice is executed? Alas what need is there of Exemplary punishment, where there are no offences committed: they need there no Lawyers, for there is never any contention, the seeds thereof, if any begin to sprout, being presently by the wisedome of the next superior puld up by the roots.

And as little need is there of Physitians; they never misdiet themselves, their Ayre is alwaies temperate and pure, neither is there any occasion at all of sicknes, as to me it seemed at least, for I could not heare that ever any of them were sicke. But the time that nature hath assigned unto them being spent, without any paine at all they die, or rather (I should say) cease to live, as a candle to give light, when that which nourisheth it is consumed.

I was once at the departure of one of them, which I wondred much to behold; for notwithstanding the happy life hee led, and multitude of friends and children hee should forsake, as soone as certainely hee understood and perceived his end to approach, hee prepared a great feast, and calling about him all those hee especially esteemed of, hee bids them be merry and rejoyce with him, for that the time was come he should now leave the counterfeit pleasures of that world, and bee made partaker of all true joyes and perfect happinesse.

I wondred not so much at his constancy, as the behaviour of those his friends: with us in the like case, all seeme to mourne, when often some of them doe but laugh in their sleeves, or as one says, under a vizard. But here, young and old, both seemingly, and in my conscience, sincerely did rejoyce thereat, so as if any dissembled, it was but their owne griefe conceived for their owne particular losse. Their bodies being dead putrifie not, and therefore are not buried, but kept in certaine roomes ordained for that purpose; so as most of them can shew their Ancestors' bodies uncorrupt for many generations.

There is never any raine, wind, or change of the Ayre, never either Summer, or Winter, but as it were a perpetuall Spring, yeelding all pleasure, all content, and that free from any annoyance at all.

O my Wife and Children, what wrong have you done mee to bereave mee of the happinesse of that place: but it maketh no matter, for by this voyage am I sufficiently assured, that ere long the race of my mortall life being run, I shall attaine a greater happinesse elsewhere, and that everlasting.

It was the Ninth day of September that I began to ascend from El Pico; twelve dayes I was upon my Voyage, and arrived in that Region of the Moone, that they call Simiri, September the 21 following. The 12 day of May being Friday, wee came unto the Court of the great Irdonozur, and returned backe the Seventeenth unto the palace of Pylonas. There I continued till the moneth of March, in the yeare 1601, at what time I earnestly besought Pylonas (as I had often done before) to give mee leave to depart, (though with never so great hazard of my life) backe into the earth againe.

Hee much disswaded mee, laying before mee the danger of the voyage, the misery of that place from whence I came, and the abundant happinesse of that I now was in; But the remembrance of my Wife and Children overweighed all these reasons, and to tell you the truth, I was so farre forth moved with a desire of that deserved glory, that I might purchase at my return, as me thought I deserved not the name of a Spanyard, if I would not hazard 20 lives, rather than lose but a little possibility of the same. Wherefore I answered him, that my desire of seeing my Children was such, as I knew I could not live any longer, if I were once out of hope of the same. When then he desired one yeares stay longer, I told him it was manifest I must depart now or never: My Birds began to droope, for want of their wonted migration, 3 of them were now dead, and if a few more failed, I was for ever destitute of all possibilitie of returning.

With much adoe at last hee condescended unto my request, having first acquainted the great Irdonozur with my desire, then perceiving by the often baying of my Birds, a great longing in them to take their flight; I trimmed up mine Engine, and took my leave of Pylonas, who (for all the courtesie hee had done mee) required of mee but one thing, which was faithfully to promise him, that if ever I had meanes thereunto, I should salute from him Elizabeth, whom he tearmed the great Queene of England, calling her the most glorious of all women living, and indeed hee would often question with mee of her, and therein delighted so much, as it seemed hee was never satisfied in talking of her; hee also delivered unto mee a token or present for her of no small Value: Though I account her an enemy of Spayne, I may not faile of performing this promise as soone as I shall bee able so to doe.

Upon the 29 day of March, being Thursday, 3 dayes after my awakeing from the last Moones light, I fastened my selfe to mine Engine, not forgetting to take with mee, besides the Jewels Irdonozur had given mee (with whose use and vertues Pylonas had acquainted mee at large) a small quantitie of Victual, whereof afterward I had great use as shall bee declared. An infinite multitude of people, (and amongst the rest Pylonas himselfe being present), after I had given him the last Farewell, I let loose the raines unto my Birds, who with great greedinesse taking wing quickly carried mee out of their sight, it fel out with me as in my first passage, I never felt either hunger or thirst, till I arrived in China upon a high mountaine, some 5 Leagues from the high and mighty City of Pachin.

This Voyage was performed in lesse then 9 dayes; I heard no newes by the way of these ayrie men I had seen in my ascending. No thing stayed my journey any whit at all: Whether it was the earnest desire of my Birds to return to the Earth, where they had missed one season, or that the attraction of the Earth, so much stronger then that of the Moone, furthered thair labour; so it came to passe, although now I had 3 Birds wanting of those I carried forth with mee.

For the first 8 dayes my Birds flew before, and I with the Engine was as it were drawne by them. The Ninth day when I began to approach unto the Clouds, I perceived my selfe and mine Engine to sincke towards the Earth, and goe before them. I was then horribly afraid, lest my Birds not being able to beare our weight, they being so few, should bee constrained to precipitate both mee and themselves headlong to the Earth: wherefore I thought it no lesse then needfull to make use of the Ebelus, (one of the stones bestowed upon me by Irdonozur), which I clapped to my bare flesh within my hose: and it appeared manifestly thereupon unto mee that my Birds made their way with much greater ease then before, as being lightned of a great burthen; neither doe I thinke it possible for them to have let mee downe safely unto the Earth without that helpe.

China is a Country so populous, as I thinke there is hardly a peece of ground to bee found, (in the most barren parts of the same) though but thrice a man's length, which is not most carefully manured. I being yet in the Ayre, some of the country people had espied mee, and came running unto mee by troopes, they seised upon mee, and would needs, by and by, carrie mee unto an Officer. I seeing no other remedy, yeelded my selfe unto them. But when I assayed to goe, I found my selfe so light, that I had much adoe, one foote being upon the ground, to set downe the other, that was by reason of my Ebelus, so applyed, as it tooke quite away all weight and ponderousnesse from my body: Wherefore bethinking my selfe what was to be done, I fained a desire of performing the necessitie of nature, which by signes being made knowen unto them (for they understood not a word of any Language I could speake) they permitted mee to goe aside among a few bushes, assuring themselves that for mee to escape from them it was impossible; Being there I remembred the directions Pylonas had given mee, concerning the use of my stones, and first I tooke them all together, with a few Jewells yet remaining of those I had brought out of India, and knit them up in my handkerchiefe, all, except one the least and worst Ebelus. Him I found meanes to apply in such sort unto my body, as but the halfe of his side touched my skin, whereby it came to passe that my body then had but halfe the weight, that being done I drew towards these my Guardians, till seeing them come somewhat neere together they could not crosse my way, I shewed them a faire paire of heeles.

This I did to the end I might recover an opportunitie of finding my Stones, and Jewells, which I knew they would rob mee off, if I prevented them not. Being thus lightned I bid them such a base, as had they been all upon the backes of so many Race-Horses, they could never have overtaken mee. I directed my course unto a certaine thicke wood, into which I entred some quarter of a League, and then finding a pretty spring, (which I tooke for my marke), hard by it, I thrust my jewells into a little hole made by a Mole, or some such like creature. Then I tooke out of my pocket my Victualls, (to which in all my Voyage I had not till then any desire) and refreshed my selfe therewith, till such time as the people pursuing mee, had over-taken mee, into whose hands I quietly delivered my selfe.

They led mee unto an inferior Officer, who (understanding that once I had escaped from them that first apprehended mee), caused a certaine seat to be made of boords, into which they closed mee in such sort, as onely my head was at liberty, and then carried mee upon the shoulders of 4 slaves, (like some notorious malefactor) before a man of great authority, whom in their language as after I learned, they called a Mandarine, abiding 2 dayes journey off, to wit one League distant from the great and famous City of Pachin, or Paquin, by the Chinesse called Suntien.

Their language I could no way understand; onely this I could discerne, that I was for something or other accused with a great deale of vehemence. The substance of this accusation it seemes was, that I was a Magician, as witnessed my strange carriage in the ayre; that being a stranger, as appeared by my both language and habit, I contrary to the Lawes of China, entred into the Kingdome without warrant, and that probably with no good intent. The Mandarine heard them out, with a great deale of composed gravitie; and being a man of quicke apprehension, and withall studious of novelties, hee answered them, that hee would take such order with mee, as the case required, and that my bold attempt should not want its deserved punishment. But having dismissed them he gave order to his Servants, that I should be kept in some remote parts of his vast Palace, and bee strictly watched, but courteously used: This doe I conjecture, by what at the present I found, and what after followed. For my accommodation was every way better than I could expect; I lodged well, fared well, was attended well, and could not fault any thing, but my restraint. In this manner did I continue many moneths, afflicted with nothing so much as with the thought of my Gansas; which I knew must be irrecoverably lost, as indeed they were. But in this time, by my owne industry, and the forwardnesse of those that accompanied me, I learnt to speak indifferently the language of that Province, (for almost every Province in China, hath its proper Language) whereat I discerned they tooke no small content.

I was at length permitted to take the ayre, and brought into the spacious garden of that Palace, a place of excellent pleasure, and delight, as being planted with herbes and Flowers of admirable both sweetnes and beauty, and almost infinite variety of fruits both European and others, and all those composed with that rare curiositie, that I was ravished with the contemplation of such delightfull objects. But I had not here long recreated my selfe, when the Mandarine entred the Garden, on that side where I was walking, and being advertised thereof by his servants, and wished to kneel down unto him (as I after found it to be the usuall publique reverence to those great Officers) I did so, and humbly craved his favour towards a poore stranger, that arrived in those parts, not by his own destination, but by the secret disposall of the heavens: Hee in a different language (which all the Mandarines, as I have since learned, do use) and that like that of the Lunars did consist much of tunes, but was by one of his servants interpreted to mee. Hee, I say, wished mee to bee of good comfort, for that he intended no harme unto mee, and so passed on. The next day I was commanded to come before him, and so conducted into a sumptuous dining roome exquisitely painted and adorned. The Mandarine having commanded all to avoide the roome, vouchsafed conference with mee in the vulgar language; inquiring first the estate of my Country, the power of my Prince, the religion and manners of the people; wherein being satisfied by mee, hee at last descended to the particulars of my education and studies, and what brought mee into this remote countrey: Then did I at large declare unto him the adventure of my life, only omitting here and there, what particulars I thought good, forbearing especialy any mention of the stones given me by Irdonozur. The strangenes of my story did much amaze him. And finding in all my discourse nothing any way tending to Magique; (wherein he had hoped by my means to have gained some knowledge) he began to admire the excellence of my wit, applauding me for the happiest man that this world had ever produced: and wishing me to repose my selfe after my long narration, he for that time dismissed me.

After this, the Mandarine tooke such delight in me, that no day passed, wherein he sent not for me. At length he advised me to apparell my selfe in habit of the Country (which I willingly did) and gave mee not onely the liberty of his house, but took mee also abroad with him, when he went to Paquin, whereby I had the opportunitie by degrees to learn the disposition of the people, and the policie of the Country, which I shall reserve for my second part. Neither did I by this my attendance on him gaine only the knowledge of these things, but the possibility also of being restored to my native soyle, and to those deare pledges which I value above the world, my Wife and children. For by often frequenting Paquin, I at length heard of some Fathers of the Society of Iesus that were become famous for the extraordinary favour by the King vouchsafed them, to whom they had presented some European trifles, as Clockes, Watches, Dials, and the like, which with him passed for exquisite rarities. To them by the Mandarine's leave I repaired, was welcomed by them, they much wondring to see a Lay Spaniard there, whither they had with so much difficulty obtained leave to arrive. There did I relate to father Pantoja, and those others of the society, these fore-related adventures, by whose directions I put them in writing, and sent this story of my fortunes to Macao, from thence to be conveighed for Spaine, as a forerunner of my returne. And the Mandarine being very indulgent unto me, I came often unto the Fathers, with whom I consulted about many secrets. With them also did I lay a foundation for my returne, the blessed houre whereof I doe with patience expect; that by inriching my Country with the knowledge of hidden mysteries, I may once reape the glory of my fortunate misfortunes.

FINIS

Select Bibliography

Benson, E.G., 'The Brasses of Burghill, Herefordshire',
   Transactions of the Monumental Brass Society, 1947, 171-176
Blake, W.A., *Parish of Burghill, Herefordshire* (pamphlet guide),
   1972
Boorstin, Daniel J., *The Discoverers*, Dent, 1984
Browne Willis, *Survey of the Cathedrals*, 1742
Bruton, John, *History of the Antiquities of the Cathedral Church of
   Hereford*, 1831
Canaan, E., *Churches of the South Atlantic Islands 1502-1991*,
   Anthony Nelson, 1992
Cross, T., *St. Helena*, Newton Abbot, 1980
Dictionary of National Biography
Duncumb, *Collections towards the History & Antiquities of the
   County of Hereford, Vol. 4, Hundred of Grimsworth* (2 pts), 1886
   & 1892
Hackluytt, R., *The Principal Navigations, Voyages, traffiques and
   discoveries of the English Nation made by sea or overland*, 1599
Hanbury Brown, R., *Man and the Stars*, Oxford University Press,
   1978
Moore, Patrick, *The Guiness Book of Astronomy*, Guiness, 1992
The New Cambridge Modern History, Vol III 1559-1610

Other books from Logaston Press

Owain Glyn Dŵr
& The War of Independence in the Welsh borders

by Geoffrey Hodges, this book concentrates on the main characters, the background to and the actual fighting in the borders. 256pp with photographs. £9.95. ISBN 1 873827 24 5

The Civil War in Hereford

by Ron Shoesmith. Documents from the Civil War are used to tell the history of the four sieges by Parliament of Hereford together with the accompanying strife in the county as a whole. 176pp with maps and photographs. £8.95. ISBN 1 873827 34 2

A View from Hereford's Past

by Richard Stone and Nic Appleton-Fox, this is the interim archaeological report of the excavation at Hereford Cathedral in preparation for the building of the new Mappa Mundi exhibition centre. It relates several surprising finds. 80pp with 44 photographs, maps and illustrations. (A4 format) £9.95. ISBN 1 873827 39 3

The Monuments in the Landscape series

A series of detailed guides which will expand to include several subjects on each side of the Welsh border. Currently available are:

Vol. 1 Prehistoric Sites of Herefordshire

by George Children and George Nash. 144pp with some 50 photographs, plans and maps. £6.95. ISBN 1 873827 09 1

Vol. II Castles & Moated Sites of Herefordshire

by Ron Shoesmith. 256pp with some 65 photographs, plans and maps. £9.95. ISBN 1 873827 59 8

Vol. III Castles of Radnorshire

by Paul Remfry. 160pp with some 35 photographs, plans and maps. £7.95. ISBN 1 873827 54 7

Vol. IV Prehistoric Sites of Monmouthshire

by George Children and George Nash. 144pp with some 40 photographs, plans and maps. £7.95. ISBN 1 873827 49 0